The People's Potatoes

Alan Wilson

Alan has studied and promoted the potato for more than 30 years within his agricultural and technical role for Waitrose supermarkets and as a hobby. His work in agriculture has promoted organic farming, close working relationships with growers, and the promotion of British food. His passion for potatoes showed itself in his first book, *The Story of the Potato* (1993). He was a founder member of 'Potato Days', launched by Henry Doubleday Research Association (now Garden Organic), and writes and lectures regularly.

Dr Simon Bowen

After studying at London University, Simon went on to complete a PhD on cyst nematodes and crop pests before embarking on a career spanning some 25 years to date working alongside commercial potato growers as an adviser and research scientist. He has worked extensively with seed and ware growers in Scotland and ware growers in England as well as in Europe. He is passionate about ensuring that the best commercial production methods are based on sound science. Based in Lincolnshire, Simon is currently Technical Director of a company growing and packing fresh potatoes for the UK retail market.

Caroline Bletsis

Caroline is self-taught from an artistic family who specialise in wild and domestic animal paintings. She also paints landscapes, portraits and still life.

Caroline is a member of the Fleet Art Society and the Wildlife Art Society, and has exhibited paintings at the London Zoological Society, Bristol Zoo, Port Lympne Zoo, the Mall Galleries, Patchings Art Festival and Best of Hampshire Artists at Hillier Gardens, Romsey.

For seven years running Caroline has been selected to be exhibited in the national wildlife painting competition PAWS, and won the Best Watercolour in 2003 and the Joyce Chaffin Award in the 2004 'all-time winners' final PAWS exhibition.

The People's Potatoes

Alan Wilson

With paintings by Caroline Bletsis

Alan Wilson

ACKNOWLEDGEMENTS

The artist Caroline Bletsis has lovingly created the majority of the portraits of the potato varieties, capturing their distinguishing features. I am in no doubt that the text is second to these paintings, which were created over a two-year period in line with the growing trials of the lesser-known varieties. Having a typical example of a variety from a small sample did prove a challenge. The paintings of Arran Consul, Arran Victory, Duke of York, Dunbar Rover, Red Salad Potato, Kerr's Pink and Wilja were painted by Faith Harris, and first appeared in *The Story of the Potato* (Alan Wilson, 1993).

Dr Simon Bowen has more than cast his eye over this book, offering recommendations at all stages. With his characteristic enthusiasm he has written the chapter on the potato plant. Having worked in Scotland and become immersed in the subject for most of his working life, he is more than qualified. It has been great to debate the numerous slants and balances that this subject throws up. I count myself privileged to know a person with such knowledge.

I do not think it gets much better than being brought a bacon sandwich while standing in the middle of the variety trial plots in Edinburgh. The team at SASA (Science & Advice for Scottish Agriculture) have been fantastic in providing help and access. I single out Maureen McCreath and Sandra Goodfellow, two people with outstanding potato knowledge and heaps of kindness. The photo illustrations of pests and diseases have also been kindly supplied by SASA, and I am grateful to Sylvia Breslin for her help in that regard. Exceptions are those on page 17, supplied by Diana Thomas.

The most honest critics and supporters are my own family and I am grateful for their comments along the way and for reading and discussing at all hours of the day and night.

First published in 2011

British Library Cataloguing in Publication Data

A catalogue record for this book is available from the British Library.

ISBN 978 0 9520973 1 0

Edited and designed by

Priory Ash Publishing
2 Denford Ash Cottages
Denford
Kettering
Northamptonshire NN14 4EW
01832 734425
www.prioryash.co.uk

in association with

Silver Link Publishing Ltd
The Trundle
Ringstead Road
Great Addington
Kettering
Northamptonshire NN14 4BW
01536 330543

Printed and bound in the Czech Republic

CONTENTS

Potato harvesting at College Farm, Duxford.

FOREWORD

by
Colin Randel
Vegetable Product Manager, Thompson & Morgan, Ipswich

I feel honoured that Alan has asked me to write this foreword. I have worked in the horticultural trade all of my working life, predominantly in the vegetable seed industry. For over 20 years potatoes have played a major part, although planting Home Guards and King Edwards as a youngster for my gran is ingrained in my memory.

My first acquaintance with Alan goes back to HDRA, where his career with Waitrose has encompassed his passion for potatoes, and through which Waitrose sponsored HDRA's Potato Days. These were pioneering, innovative days whereby HDRA (now Garden Organic) displayed a wide choice of varieties for sale by the tuber to their members and the general public. I regularly helped out during these weekends and the format has over the years spread to all parts of Britain, with themed Potato Days and selling by the tuber. This does give gardeners a chance to be adventurous and to try a number of varieties in any one season and assess different tastes, textures, skin and flesh colours, and tuber shapes and sizes.

With *The People's Potatoes* Alan has written about his own experiences of a large number of varieties and portrays his preferences in a passionate style. The accompanying lovely pictures must surely tempt readers (and gardeners) to be just that tad more inquisitive and experiment with a change of variety. In many instances they may well find one that tastes and yields better than their traditional favourites. Alan has grown and assessed a wide number of varieties, some even not even known to me!

I am proud of my involvement in potatoes through Thompson & Morgan seed suppliers. We have played a leading role in offering to gardeners heritage varieties as microplants or heritage minitubers. However, we have also pioneered the sale of the Mayan 'phureja' varieties and the Sarpo blight-resistance programme, all of which Alan has included.

My earliest contacts were with Phoenix (now WCF Phoenix) and Hendersons of Dumfries. Varietal choices were relatively limited, perhaps 25 or so, compared to more than 250 today. Certainly in recent years the breeders, recognising the growing importance of the garden trade, have 'opened up' and host regular trials and events whereby their new breeding programmes are displayed and discussed with a view that gardeners will be offered them. This augurs well for the future. I believe that Alan, and through his first book back in 1993, made a significant contribution to potato variety awareness. *The People's Potatoes* is a natural progression, with some really interesting facts about commercial potato growing and some down-to-earth detail on pests and diseases.

This book is a must for those gardeners wishing to experience that incomparable 'fresh from the soil' taste and the reward of growing their own. Chapter 4 provides easy-to-read guidelines on how to grow successfully. The 'grow your own' phenomenon moves relentlessly on and, as the waiting list for an allotment in many parts of the country shows, now is the time to try potato-growing yourself.

The People's Potatoes is both a fantastic reference book with its easy-to-find A-to-Z variety list and an indispensable and inspiring guide. Alan's passion is a tribute to the humble potato – hopefully gardeners will go out and source, grow and enjoy some of these treasures. The reward will not just be discovering new tastes, colours and textures, but also helping to keep alive the diversity of our most famous of staple foods.

Colin Randel

PS My favourite potato of all time is Red Duke of York, for its taste whether lifted as an early, second early or maincrop…

INTRODUCTION:
A NEW POTATO BOOK!

Welcome and thank you for your interest in the wonderful potato. It is nearly 20 years since *The Story of the Potato* was published, its objective having been to raise awareness of potato varieties. *The People's Potatoes* expands and develops that theme with a new and extensive collection of individual potato variety paintings, variety descriptions and information on growing potatoes.

Whether in my own garden or visiting a large field in Lincolnshire, the potato is for me simply a fascinating plant and food. Behind it is an industry of change, enthusiasm, science and people dedicated to producing crops to feed us.

Despite our nation's obsession with wheat, our delight with rice and our indulgence with meat, the potato remains the answer to the world's food issues. It is a low-energy crop to produce and its final yield is higher than its rivals. Against crops such as wheat, corn and rice it needs the least water and gives the most calories. The water requirement for 1kg of meat production is at least 20 times that of fresh potatoes. Despite the natural advantage, we increasingly use the potato processed as crisps, frozen chips and ready-made meals. This form of use raises questions concerning the impact on diet and energy use.

The People's Potatoes contains a highly personal selection of more than 400 varieties mostly chosen from around 1,200 in the SASA (Science & Advice for Scottish Agriculture) reference collection at East Craigs. There are new commercial varieties being introduced every year and each one is different from the 5,000 varieties recorded.

I have split the variety list into two sections. The first contains an alphabetical 'Top 100' of varieties with which we are familiar (together with some not so familiar). These are the varieties that have made, or are currently making, a real contribution to potato-growing in the UK. It's an arbitrary list with no real rules. Some are my favourites and some certainly are not. What would be in your Top 100? Is your favourite potato variety still grown? A secondary descriptive list of more than 300 covers old, new and lesser known-varieties.

I have believed for some time that people's access to old potato varieties should be free from rules and red tape. Essentially it is a commercial decision. If we support old varieties, by buying or growing them, someone will organise the plantings of high-grade seed or micro-tubers. I am not saying that old varieties have all the answers. However, if they are not available to the public, we remove the diversity and the chance for a wider group of people to experience the challenges, requirements and joys of different potatoes. Through micro-plants and mini-tubers, we do have the means to produce and distribute small quantities. If our attitude to the potato is indifferent, we will only have ourselves to blame if one day the world of the potato is an anonymous 'red' or an imported 'white'.

The range of potato varieties

The resurgence of interest in the potato, particularly old varieties. is thrilling to experience. Back in the 1980s we nearly lost all our old varieties as they were duly removed from the UK national list, which controlled what could be sold as a seed potato. Many are now back by public demand, but many more are still hidden away and their potential remains largely unexplored. Varieties such as Duke of York, Red Duke of York, Dunbar Rover, Pink Fir Apple, Fortyfold, Highland Burgundy Red, Shetland Black, Vitelotte, Arran Victory and many more are now available as seed for gardeners and commercial growers.

There is no definition of what 'old' or 'heritage' means. So here is my interpretation. A variety can be called old when it is at least 50 years of age. Potato seed can be obtained from garden centres or through mail order; buy as soon as they are in stock. The visual diversity of potato varieties makes for some striking natural images and enthusiastic debate. Taste, so often the missing component of new varieties, is a prominent feature of older types, but by no means all – many were discarded for reasons of taste.

Two most interesting and famous potato varieties are Jersey Royal (which is identical to International Kidney) and King Edward, which together have a combined historical exposure of more than 200 years. They have remained ever-present and viable entirely due to their fantastic taste. If grown properly and eaten at the right time the flavour is simply a taste sensation and one of the most satisfying experiences of life.

The variety Kestrel remains a towering example of how progress in variety breeding can advance agronomy and taste. Yet there are many others produced each year that are worth closer inspection. Taste is, of course, subjective, so that is another reason to try out the new as well as the old.

The relatively new Hungarian varieties prefixed 'Sarpo' (Mira, Axona, etc) have amazing blight resistance. Their culinary performance received mixed reviews, but if it is blight resistance that you are after then this range is a major step forward. Another most interesting addition to potato diversity has been the inclusion in breeding programmes of the second most popular species in Peru, *Solanum phureja*. The breeders at SCRI have made great efforts to overcome the short dormancy and have produced several new interesting varieties.

The taste of a potato of any variety can be influenced by a range of agronomic factors. These include variety maturity, soil type, nutrients, water availability, water quality, temperature during growing, harvest, and storage. Therefore I have to stress that all the variety comments in this book are only a base, and the true worth of a variety is proven by time and knowledge of which growing regime works best. Finding the most appropriate fit for your expectations is part of the fun. I hope this book is helpful in that regard.

Fresh or processed?

There have been two massive impacts upon recent potato variety development. The first is that our buying habit has dramatically changed. Despite all the noise about health, we as a nation are consuming fewer fresh potatoes – those that you buy in the pre-packs from supermarkets or the farm shop. Instead we are buying processed potatoes in the form of chips, crisps and prepared meals. Do you know the variety inside the packet of chips or crisps? Where was it grown?

In every developed country there is a dramatic fall in fresh potato consumption and a rise in potatoes used in processed foods. In 1993 each person in the UK consumed 72kg of fresh and 36kg of processed. By 2009 it had changed to 43kg and 48kg respectively. It is the consequence of the decline of the family meal, and the rise of wheat, pasta and rice products. It is no surprise that of the ten top potato varieties grown in

the UK in 2008, five are entirely bred and used for processing. If I ever come round again for a third book (let's say 2025…) my prediction is that fresh potato consumption within the UK commercial sector is likely to account for only 25kg per person per year. The use of the potato for starch content and industrial use will become an increasingly important part of variety breeding.

Refreshingly, I expect the seed potato market for gardeners to rise. With the increase in food security issues, the days of cheap food may be behind us. The natural human desire within us all to grow food may just be reawakening. If that is the case there is even more reason to cherish the varieties we have access to now to ensure that the potatoes of the people are maintained for the people.

A changing market

The second dramatic change is the route to market for the potato. Britain used to be covered in hundreds of thousands of small greengrocers, each one a unique and independent point of contact with the customer. These largely privately owned High Street shops sourced their requirement from the many provincial wholesale markets.

Today this is strikingly different, with 92% of all fresh potatoes being sold through supermarkets. So the route for a new variety to market is narrow. The decision for stocking a new variety is based on corporate interpretations of consumer needs, and while there is some variety difference between retailers, there is also much similarity.

Genetic modification

The obvious challenge for potato variety breeders is going to be the adoption (or not) of genetically modified organisms (GMOs). At present the only potato variety that can be grown within the EU that has been genetically modified is for industrial use; that variety is called Amflora and its development underlines the growing importance of the potato in manufacturing: the production of starch in stable and consistent quantities by genetic modification is attractive in its commercial potential and application.

Since potato plant breeding began, the genetic make-up of a variety has been changing. It is regrettable that the simple phrase 'genetically modified organism' covers everything from within a species to genetic movement across species. There are around 200 potato species in the world, most of them inedible but containing many traits that could really help farmers and growers. Many current varieties owe their existence to the inclusion of different potato species sourced from visits to Peru and Chile during the last century.

Blight, potato cyst nematodes, insects and other key causes of crop waste and input losses could be addressed. For example, some varieties can be shallow-rooting and hence very susceptible to fluctuations in soil moisture content. Within the wild species genome this could be fixed, which could offer a massive potential in reducing the water requirement. Could this be achieved more quickly by adopting GMOs, rather than a traditional cross-pollination route? However, to date the most prominent example of the GMO application to the potato has been the herbicide (weedkiller) resistance applied to Russet Burbank; this engendered much criticism and was withdrawn.

Whether GM in potatoes will happen may depend on you. Could such a technology play a part in helping this world develop in harmony, or will its introduction simply prove too divisive and too linked to big business at the expense of small to medium-sized producers? The introduction of dramatically higher-yielding genetically modified varieties has thrown up social and economic issues in some countries comparable to the Industrial Revolution of 250 years ago. If we are to accept GM, we have to manage the aspects and impacts such developments could bring.

Gardening is a growing hobby

This leads us into a personal passion of mine, which is growing vegetables. Whether in the garden, allotment, container, greenhouse or cloche, I encourage everyone to 'have a go'. Since the last book was published it seems that the nation has reawakened its passion for growing and knowing about food. There are waiting lists for allotments, and in the spring a massive range of vegetable seeds and plants is available. This is to be welcomed, but there is still much more to be done.

In an age of carbon-consciousness, there is no better contribution we can make than by growing our own food, or at least making a start. People who grow potatoes tend to make the most of them in terms of utilisation. The green bits, fork damage and severe skin scabs are cut away, allowing the tuber to be used. There is generally less emphasis on the visual appearance. Of the weight of crop harvested in the garden, 95% may be used. That is very different from

the commercial world of washed potato pre-packing, where up to 47% can be rejected or discarded for use in lower-value markets or animal feed. When buying potatoes we naturally have a rather different tolerance and understanding of acceptable quality.

However, commercial growers make much better use of their inputs, producing higher yields. They have efficiencies from which the gardener can learn. Great progress has been made in reducing crop waste resulting from potato blight, storage and poor seed quality.

The secret of gardening is timing. By ensuring that you perform the right tasks at the right time, you will avoid long weeding sessions or disappointment. Remembering the importance of the soil and the place in the food chain of all species will help create a balance within the allotment, garden or farm. This book describes how farmers approach their soil and potato growing. There are potential gains for gardeners selectively adopting appropriate tricks of the trade. For farmers, thinking of their farm in the context of a garden may be a helpful reminder of public expectation.

Everyone is organic

Growing organically is not an option, it is a must. However, the closer you look at the legal definitions and rules, the more that essential ideal unfortunately becomes a real challenge. This comes at a time when food security is a key issue. Ensuring that your land is covered with green crops for soil structure and nutrition, and the critical role of organic matter, are massively important. Encouraging biodiversity is an essential component, as opposed to a cosmetic flirtation. Yet organic growing does not have a monopoly on wisdom, and this book has one eye on building a bridge between all farmers and gardeners.

Controlling pest and diseases

For amateur growers, be they organic or conventionally minded, pests and diseases remain an issue. So there is a chapter focusing on key pests, especially blight, nematodes and, of course, slugs. Apart from supporting the use of some modern blight sprays, I remain cautious about the use of insecticides, herbicides and, to a degree, fungicides. The chapter about pests and diseases is really all about minimising the use of chemicals by taking precautions. There is much we can do to prevent pest build-up or the inadvertent creation of disease pressure. This has been the premise of the organic movement: healthy soil equals healthy plants.

The need for seed

A good knowledge of seed production is essential for good potato-growing. So we look at how seed is produced, why there are so many controls, and why it is one of the few bits of agriculture the Government still engage in rather than farm out to the commercial sector. Get your seed right and you remove many of the later problems. With potato seed age manipulation, you could be harvesting earlier or later and with crops of varying numbers and sizing.

Breeders

Gone are the days of state-funded potato-breeding stations. In the UK potato-breeding is now totally privately funded. Our leading UK potato-breeder over the past 40 years has been Dr Jack Dunnett. After pioneering work on the Pentland series, he was single-handedly responsible for all the varieties marketed by Caithness Potatoes. He is now retired. The overall quality of some of his varieties has set a new benchmark in agronomy and eating quality, and you will see his name come up regularly. To the legendary potato-breeders of the past – Robert Fenn, James Clark, Archibald Findlay, John Clarke, Donald Mackelvie, Charles Spence – we now add Jack Dunnett MBE.

Potato-breeding thrives in Holland and many of the varieties in this book are of Dutch origin. But there are others. Breeding is still a feature of Oak Park Research Centre, Dublin, the Scottish Crop Research Institute at Invergowrie also has new additions, and we have witnessed some dramatic new varieties in blight resistance from the Sarvari family in Hungary.

As important as potato varieties are, their breeding and adoption should not come as antidote to poor farming or growing methods. In recent years our climate has proved how excessive it can be, and this will continue. Growers need our utmost respect and support as we ensure that the food of today can be produced on land for tomorrow. If assessment of potato varieties has taught me one thing it is that time and not a trial plot will be the measure of success. The rules for all potato growers are the same whether growing one row or one field. May your potatoes be good for you and those you grow for.

Alan Wilson
Fleet, Hampshire
September 2011

CHAPTER ONE

THE COMMERCIAL POTATO GROWER

The people who grow our food

Farming as an industry and way of life has always been in a state of change. Apart from the inevitability of seasonal weather, economics has been a key driver of change. As generations of the UK population have become detached from an understanding of farming principles, the focus of interest has centred on the retail price. The narrow UK food market is controlled by a few highly competitive supermarket giants, and the focus on end-user price has, in turn, driven down returns to farmers. The strategy farmers have been encouraged to employ to mitigate such price pressure has been to intensify production and maximise their investment in machinery and infrastructure.

The number of people involved in UK commercial potato-growing has dramatically declined, a fall that continues to this day. In 1960 the UK had 76,825 commercial potato-growers. By 2009 this had fallen to 2,721, a decrease of 74,104, or 96%, which means that on average 1,482 growers are leaving the potato industry a year. This is the human cost of the relentless drive for cheap food – it affects everyone by changing the fabric of rural life. It also poses questions, such as what we want our countryside to be and how much we value the related, small, diverse industries and amenities.

It is a dramatic change that largely goes unnoticed. Unlike at the time of the Irish Famine, we now have an abundance of potatoes. We have become accustomed to having what we want as opposed to what we need. This abundance of mostly cheap potatoes can bring a lack of interest in how they are grown. We then move to a lack of appreciation of the true cost of cheap food.

We are not short of potatoes, milk, meat and home-grown foods. This is because the yields obtained have more than doubled in the past 50 years. The average area of potatoes per grower planted in 1960 was 3.65 hectares, yielding an average of 22.6 tonnes. In 2008 the average area planted per grower was 45 hectares, yielding 45.1 tonnes – a striking success story. The challenge, and in some ways the hardest part, will be the continuation and development of such yields, while at the same time ensuring the countryside's health and diversity.

One scandal of affluence is that around 47% of the commercially grown potatoes produced are never consumed by the market for which they were grown. There are huge numbers graded out for tuber damage, severe bruising, greens and other pests and diseases. Some stock may be utilised in lesser-value markets, including processing and animal feed. The leading farmers are now breaking down all aspects of inputs and identifying how the wastage can be minimised, and retailers have a responsibility to engage if not lead this process. Losses from potato blight and storage rots make up a very small percentage thanks to excellent science in the form of modern blight fungicide sprays.

Most of the UK's potato crops are grown in the 'The Larder of England': the eastern counties of the UK, Cambridgeshire, Lincolnshire and Norfolk. Some areas are classed as new potato areas, and these are Cornwall, Pembrokeshire, Suffolk and Kent. The average farm size has increased dramatically over the past 50 years; today farms of 2,000 acres are common.

Mixed farms (that is animals and potato crops) are now rare, their regrettable and dramatic decline again related to efficiency of production. Animals are a great source of organic matter, which means that, when it comes to planting potatoes, the total rotation is heavily cereal based. Sugar beet and oil seed rape are widely planted, but have little, if any, positive effect on the soil or the potato crop. So all this means that at planting time many farmers have to rely on artificial nitrogen as the key fertility element in obtaining high yields. The soluble fertiliser needs moisture, and together they drive plant growth. The widespread use of artificial fertilisers raises the issue of nitrous oxide pollution; the long-term effect upon soil biology is not widely understood. The use of heavy machinery, and the type and time of cultivation regarding soil structure is also a challenge.

E. C. Brown & Sons

E. C. Brown & Sons of Whittlesey, near Peterborough, Cambridgeshire, is typical of how farming has changed and how that change manifests itself. The farm is highly rated for the quality of crop produced and the dedication and care each crop receives. On this farm onions play an important soil-cleansing role within the rotation. The growers, Jonathan and Robert Brown, take up the story:

E. C. Brown & Sons is now a fourth-generation farming business. We were established in the late 1800s by Zacheus Brown, when he started farming at 'Crease Bank' near Peterborough, moving to Wypemere Farm in 1911. In that year Wypemere Farm was just 18.5 hectares (45 acres). Zaccy's son, Ernest Cecil Brown (ECB), grew the farm to approximately 44.5 hectares (110 acres), then alongside him his sons Brian, Michael and John expanded the farms to around 243 hectares (600 acres).

In 1982 we joined the partnership with our fathers, Michael and Brian. During this time the acreage has moved up to approximately 647 hectares (1,600 acres) through land purchases and farming arrangements with neighbouring farmers.

We now operate the business to supply major supermarkets with high-quality products from the fenland area. We have a high investment in the latest cold storage, machinery and people.

Our crops are potatoes (6,100 tonnes – Maris Piper, King Edward, Red King Edward, Kestrel, Mozart, Estima, Sante and Vivaldi); onions (2,500 tonnes, aiming for the pre-packing outlets and growing mainly brown-bulb onions and a small production area of shallots); sugarbeet (11,000 tonnes); dried peas (250 tonnes, some grown for seed production and for animal feed); and winter wheat (3,000 tonnes, all for animal feed markets).

Water

Whether you are a commercial grower or an allotment gardener, the availability of water will be key to your success. To produce the best potatoes, water in terms of soil-holding capacity and timely application will be as important as site selection, seed health and variety choice.

Water is a key issue in modern farming. Before 1976, the year of a severe UK drought, main crop yields were 25 tonnes per hectare. Ten years later, with investment in irrigation equipment, yields were pushing 40 tonnes per hectare. Other reasons for the increased yield are variety choice, the control of late blight, use of pesticides, climate, and simply good agricultural practice. Most commentators agree that 1976 was a defining year in potato-growing and that the use of water in potato production has dramatically increased yields and improved cosmetic quality.

Water has to be available as the plant requires. Within a few weeks of a hot June, stories of hosepipe bans, scorched lawns and poor crop growth make the news. The potato farmer must keep applying water, and to do this farms have increasingly invested in holding capacity through purpose-built on-farm reservoirs, filled from rivers swollen by winter rainfall and capturing water that would otherwise run out to sea. Traditional summer extraction from rivers and boreholes is likely to come under closer scrutiny and greater financial constraint.

When to apply the water is also interesting. The plant sets its tubers at a very early stage, and a lack of water or soil moisture will affect tuber numbers. An assessment of soil moisture, using tensiometers and electronic probes, will take place throughout the growing season. A large proportion of the total water applied to the growing crop is used for common scab control; this is a minor cosmetic disease described later. Water is also used to lubricate some dry soils before harvesting to reduce the impact of hard soil clogs, and is usually applied via overhead sprays. Some are very efficient, but others waste tremendous amounts through spray evaporation. Perversely, over-watering and its associated effects (powdery scab) are also a problem. Trickle irrigation is therefore making an appearance; it is a heavy investment, but the cost benefit ratio is changing in favour of this efficient and accurate method of application.

A farm that does not have a sustainable water supply combined with efficient application will be heavily penalised in market value and final yield. Water availability, application and storage will be the key discussion points for the modern grower, whether commercial or amateur.

Finally, there is recognition that the soil and its management play an essential part in water-holding capacity. Through intensive farming UK soils are low on organic matter and this is a most serious concern, leading to more water use and loss. Soils become prone to water run-off from heavy rains, and erosion

College Farm, Duxford

College Farm at Duxford, Cambridgeshire, is typical of the modern farming approach. Like E. C. Brown, it is a highly successful farm and requires more land to fill demand for its products and maintain quality. It also has a substantial acreage devoted to organic farming. Based on a long-standing relationship with a retailer (Waitrose), the farm management can plan with confidence for the future. A key element within that is planning the long-term water supply. Farmer Robert Smith has had to make some big decisions to ensure the farm's viability.

If we want to produce high-quality crops we must have a secure water supply. Summer abstraction from the River Cam and local boreholes is becoming increasingly unreliable. So we decided to work with neighbouring farmers to build a 500,000m3 (110-million-gallon) reservoir. Filled through winter rainfall, it will feed 24km of underground distribution mains to support summer irrigation on up to 18 farms.

In addition to securing the water supply, the reservoir will unlock a further 3,000 hectares of land for irrigated production. It will also allow longer rotations and that will help reduce pesticide use.

in dry weather. Soils with poor organic matter are not only leaching water but are also missing the value of the soil as the means to store and lock up carbon. The more organic matter in your soil, the greater the chance of crops rooting more deeply, contributing to soil structure, water retentiveness and carbon capture.

The growing season

Traditionally cultivation starts in the autumn with preparing the soil, the point of which is to get any previous crops worked into the soil, open the soil to the winter frosts and provide aeration. This is a skilled job and one that needs careful timing to avoid soil compaction or excessive water loss. Further soil working is performed in the spring to get the soil friable and free from lumps or clods.

Seed potatoes arrive
The stock of seed potatoes arrives in early February.

These may have been chosen from a known seed-grower in Scotland, Wales or northern England, while Holland is also a key supplier. The farmer may even have visited the growing crop. Healthy seed is critical, and too often a neglected area; seed health will be the highest priority. In addition, the tubers will be size-graded. Once purchased the seed is kept in a frost-free area. It may be placed in trays for chitting (being allowed to sprout). Many growers plant unchitted seed, which the handling and planting machines can accommodate.

Planting
A nematicide (to reduce nematode cysts) is worked into some soils. This practice is common in conventional farming due to the problem of potato cyst nematodes (PCN). Close rotations have allowed the build-up of this aggressive pest, which eats the roots of potato plants. PCN can be controlled by an integrated approach of variety resistance, use of brassica crops, growing new potatoes as a trap crop, and longer rotations. Organic farming does not permit the use of chemical nematicides.

Planting is the first big event as potato-growers, with sometimes hundreds of acres to plant, wait for the right weather window. The most common fault is planting too early. This leads to more nitrogen use and more pest and disease risk. Rows are set at least 90cm to 1 metre wide for maincrop, or sometimes they are grown in wide beds. The seed tubers are placed, usually unchitted, 30cm apart. For conventional crops, artificial fertiliser may be used at planting or supplemented during the growing season. Animal manures are used where available. After planting, an initial herbicide is applied before the potato plants appear.

The planted potatoes are then ridged to ensure a flat top area and angled sides. This is a precision operation to ensure that water reaches the potato and run-off does not erode the ridges, which could expose the growing tubers to light. Soil quality plays an important role in ridge integrity.

Control of blight
One key to the success of the modern chemical industry has been the provision of blight sprays of increasing efficiency and low environmental toxicity. These chemicals are not permitted by the European Regulation for organic farming, which has relied upon copper sulphate for the prevention of blight. Apart from the questionable blight control efficacy of copper, it inhibits the soil balance and is a soil contaminant; widespread use would have serious implications for soil health.

The modern conventional grower uses a range of blight sprays, mostly systemic, which means that the plants absorb the chemical by means of a carrier compound. Application starts when the plant is very young, and in wet seasons there is no margin for error. Where optimal crop nutrition and water availability are in place, the grower has a very fast-moving plant and the canopy being developed needs protection. An average commercial main crop will take 12 applications of a mixture of blight sprays to ensure that the foliage is kept clean and that plant resistance is not compromised. By and large, this is successful for the conventional grower. However, losses to blight are still a huge setback in organic farming, hitting yields by as much as 60%. At the time of writing I know of no efficient blight spray for gardeners or allotment holders. This is a serious setback for gardeners, who are often accused of being the source of the infections, particularly in agricultural regions.

Watering of the crop is a constant feature and overhead watering can create even more risk from blight attack. More watering creates a vicious circle resulting in more blight sprays. Some crops receive a spray to kill aphids.

Harvesting and storage

Harvesting starts when the tubers have reached the right stage of development. Usually the foliage is still very vigorous and needs to be destroyed. This is sometimes performed with a flame burner, but in the past the chemical sulphuric acid has been used. Man-made chemical desiccants to burn the growing foliage are also used. After the haulm is burned off, usually in two weeks, the main crop can be harvested. The tubers are loaded into large bulkers or 1-tonne bins ready for immediate use or storage. Long-term storage is usually at low temperatures: 3°C to 8°C, depending on intended use.

Potatoes can be kept in cold storage for 10 months, or even longer, but the UK maincrop is usually lifted in September and cleared (sold) by the following June. There are several options to avoid the tubers sprouting; a chemical applied during the growing season, a gas during storage, and a low temperature of 3°C. Ethylene fogging is a more benign way of storing potatoes, and is potentially allowing storage at slightly higher temperatures, with a saving on energy.

The potato farmer today is almost certainly a member of an independent crop assurance scheme such as Assured Produce (AP), Tesco's Nature's Choice and Marks & Spencer's Field to Fork. Linking Environment and Farming (LEAF) is another farming standard representing the best of integrated farm management. All these schemes are intended to build consumer confidence in farmers as responsible custodians of the land. Organic farming is legally controlled within the European Union. The Soil Association, through its subsidiary company, SA Cert, is a leading certification body for the UK

Changes in the market

The modern farmer is very much aware of his market or customer. The fresh potato market is now dominated by the small number of supermarkets, which demand very large tonnages, while the wholesale markets of large towns have declined. Diversity at the retail end is restricted, and the growers are restricted in their marketing options.

Ed Parker from J. Paine & Son based in Romney Marsh, Kent, has seen some dramatic changes in how potatoes from the farm get to market.

> In the 1970s we harvested daily during June and July into 55lb bags. All the potatoes were hand-lifted and at the peak season 100 lorries a week were departing for the London markets and beyond. Kent was a really important new potato source for the UK. This market has now all gone and, although we still grow potatoes, these are maincrop for supermarkets and we store on the farm.

The rise in consumption of processed potatoes (crisps and frozen chips) has seen a corresponding decline in potatoes grown for the fresh market. Potatoes for processing are grown on contract, with the prices to the farmer fixed for a given tonnage and quality requirement. Potatoes for processing now account for more than 50% of the UK market. A large proportion is imported either as potatoes for processing or as the finished processed product.

UK potato-producers are some of the most efficient in the world, with yields that reflect this position. The modern successful potato-grower will have to compete on a range of fronts, while quality, environmental stewardship and consumer engagement are the central pivots of modern farming. In addition, there is a dazzling range of legislative and administrative requirements to receive Government/EU agri scheme support payments. Finally there is the weather. We should not take our food supply for granted, or we could one day wake up and find it unavailable or manifested in a form we find objectionable.

CHAPTER TWO

THE POTATO PLANT
BY DR SIMON BOWEN

Evolution

Potato plants are easy to grow! Evolution has seen to this by ensuring that they produce tubers as a way of re-growing or reproducing. This is called vegetative reproduction, a simple solution to the survival of the species – no need for the complexities of sexual reproduction, the intricacies of pollination, the struggle for survival or the establishment of plants from small seed. The potato tuber is the heavyweight of seeds, perfectly adapted to survival and the production of new plants, and of course being a clone of the parent plant (genetically the same) it will always be a case of 'what you see is what you get'. It is a seed packed full of energy, ready to fuel the growth of a new tuber-bearing plant for feeding humans with a great source of energy and nutrition.

Potatoes are clever. Not only can they reproduce vegetatively, but they still also have the ability to flower and for cross-pollination to occur. This allows new varieties to be formed, of which there are thousands. They come in all shapes, colours and sizes, providing a huge range to grow, taste and enjoy.

Understanding the plant

To get the best out of your plants or a commercial crop of potatoes requires a little basic understanding of plant structure and how plants grow and work. You do not need to know all the scientific names, detailed plant anatomy and physiology, just the basic facts. My objective is to give you enough basic facts to help you to understand how to get the best out your potato plants, and in particular how you may want to change your growing regime or tactics to suit different varieties in different conditions.

The potatoes used mainly in cultivated production are of the species *Solanum tuberosum*. This is a Latin name and is part of a traditional system of classifying plants. The 'tuberosum' part of the name relates to the species and, as the name suggests, indicates one that produces tubers. There are about six other Solanum species that have been cultivated for their tubers. More recently, varieties from the species *Solanum phureja* have been introduced.

One of the characteristics of the potato *Solanum tuberosum* is its ability to store energy in a tuber. That energy is created by photosynthesis. This is a complex process that takes place mainly in the leaves: essentially, carbon dioxide is bound to chlorophyll (the green pigment in leaves) and converted into the sugar – sucrose – by the absorbed light energy, releasing oxygen as a by-product. As we all know, sugar is a high-energy source.

The 'powerhouse' of leaves

The most productive plants are therefore those with good production of leaves (often referred to as leaf canopy), which are efficient at absorbing light. The longer the leaves remain during the season, generally the higher the yield. Any factors such as drought, pest or disease will reduce the amount and efficiency of leaves and therefore reduce your yield.

The potato plant is made up of leaves and stems (foliage), which are collectively known as the potato haulm. The stolons join the tubers to the plant. The roots are the fibrous material attached to, and under, the plant.

The potato plant

A very wide range of foliage (leaf) types exist and, to a degree, this is variety specific. The habit (type of foliage growth) may range from low spreading or bushy compact to tall and dense. Very often early-maturing varieties have lower-growing, less extensive foliage, while maincrop varieties have a taller, fuller habit. However, do not be fooled, because foliage growth and shape can be

The potato plant. *Caroline Bletsis*

Leaf pigmentation in Vitelotte. *Diana Thomas*

influenced by other factors. The variety Wilja can in some seasons be very low and spreading while in others higher and bushy.

The pattern and colour of leaf and stem development is variable, again influenced strongly by variety characteristics. This can be classified by detailed botanical terminology and is a subject for the specialists. However, with practice you will begin to identify some of the differences – for example, recognising how the big 'mint-like' leaves of the variety Marfona differ from the more slender red-veined leaves of Desiree. Colouration of the stems or mid-ribs of leaves is always a good indicator of a coloured tuber.

The number of stems produced per plant is a variety characteristic, although other factors such as seed size and seed age will determine the number of stems. Contrast the large number of stems of a Maris Piper plant with the fewer number produced by Marfona.

Stem numbers are key

The stems are an important feature of potato plants. Why? Well, if a stem grows directly from the seed it is called a mainstem and usually produces tubers. Therefore it follows that a lot of mainstems in a variety equates to a lot of tubers. Maris Piper produces a lot of stems and on a standard-size seed this can result in more than 20 tubers being produced, twice the number of varieties producing fewer stems. Managing the stem numbers is therefore an important part of growing potatoes. If

a stem branches from the mainstem it is called a secondary stem, and these do not usually produce tubers unless they branch from the mainstem very close to the seed. Depending on whether you want lots of small potatoes, or larger bakers, it becomes clear that managing stem numbers is key.

Potatoes reproduce vegetatively by producing tubers, and every tuber is genetically the same as the parent plant – a clone. Potatoes can also reproduce sexually via pollination of their flowers, and this is the way by which new varieties are produced. Potato plants can produce flowers, but not all varieties do. The frequency of flowering and colour and structure of the flower depends on

The flowers of Salad Blue. *Diana Thomas*

the variety, and experts can identify varieties by their flowers. Some varieties such as Maris Piper produce a mass of purple flowers; the high number of purple flowering fields seen in the Fens in mid-June is a testament to the traditional home of this variety. However, you will have to look a lot harder to recognise the crops of King Edwards with their less frequent, small, purple-tipped white flowers.

Key growth stage

The tuber is formed at an early stage in the plant's development, at a point known as tuber initiation, usually about three to four weeks after the plant has first emerged above ground. At this stage the plant has developed underground stems known as stolons, and it is these that stop growing in length and start to enlarge with cells that then become the storage sites for energy in the form of starch. Sugars produced by the growing plant are transported to the tubers and are converted into starch. Typically, in a mature tuber the starch content is about 18-20% of the tuber weight. This again varies between varieties, from the lower starch content of early-maturing varieties such as Maris Peer to the later-maturing varieties such as King Edward.

As already discussed, to fuel the growth of the tubers requires plants to establish good leaf canopies, which can efficiently intercept light, and good root systems, which can extract the required amounts of water and nutrients. The ability of plants to intercept light is affected by the structure of the canopy and how much of the ground is covered by green leaves. Some varieties have a very erect upright leaf canopy, others a more sprawling lower-growing canopy.

The growing tuber: the 'Mars a day' principle

Getting the canopy established as quickly as possible will ensure a good start to tuber growth, or what is termed 'tuber bulking'. Tuber bulking increases as the leaf canopy becomes fully established and is usually at its peak when the ground is fully covered by leaf area. This is often called full canopy, or canopy 'closed'.

Under conditions of adequate water, nutrition and the absence of any pest and disease pressure, the leaves can be very productive and can put on up to 800kg per hectare per day. Put another way, this equates approximately to 80 grams per square metre, or alternatively a large chocolate bar per square metre per day – an impressive rate of growth! And remember that the chocolate bar comparison is relevant because in the plant this production is sugar as well.

Of course, not all the tuber is sugar converted into starch. There are many other essential nutrients, such as vitamins and fibre. There is also a lot of water – typically, a tuber contains about 80% water, which is often referred to as having a dry matter of 20%. Dry matter content is very variety-specific, with earlier-maturing varieties having lower dry matter than later-maturing maincrop varieties. The dry matter has considerable influence on the cooking properties of the tuber, and this is dealt with later.

The art of dying

When the plant reaches the end of its growing cycle, the foliage will die back first. The lower leaves and the older part of the plant turn yellow with brown spots on their surfaces. This process is often termed as 'senescence' and is controlled by naturally occurring growth-inhibiting chemicals in the plant. Pests and diseases can also cause the foliage to die back, and this may be confused with natural dieback or senescence. Remember that natural senescence occurs from the bottom of the plant up. If the lower leaves look healthy and the upper leaves are turning yellow, you will need to investigate further for the cause, whether it be drought, deficient nutrition, pest or disease.

When plants die back the tubers form or set a skin around themselves to give protection against damage, pests and disease. The skin is a specialist layer of cells that are dead on the outside and have a waxy substance called suberin deposited in the cell walls, which helps to create a watertight protective layer. This process takes about two to four weeks depending on the level of senescence. Logically, if a plant is more senesced, the process will be quicker as the plant is already part the way through the process of 'shutting down'.

Obviously, plants harvested before they have senesced will have unset skins, or what is termed loose or fluffy skins. This is great if you are going to eat them fresh. However, if you want to store the potatoes for any length of time you should aim to set the skins. This will prevent water loss and the tuber going soft, and will also reduce the risk of disease infection.

There is therefore a skill in managing how your potato crops die. Harvest your earlies while the leaves are still dark green for a thin, light, fluffy skin, or ensure that you have well-set skins on the potatoes you intend to store. You can of course manipulate the process of senescence by how much water and fertiliser nutrition you give or withhold from plants, or just let the season and the weather do this for you. The skill of growing and farming is to manage this to give you the best yield of the right tuber maturity at the optimum time for harvest. This inevitably falls somewhere between art and science.

The inner potato

Nutritionally, the potato is best known for its carbohydrate content. The dry matter content of a tuber is a measure of the solid as opposed to the water content, and usually ranges between 18% and 24%. The carbohydrate or starch content is by far the biggest component of the dry matter. However, it would be wrong to overlook the fact that the tuber also contains a number of essential nutrients such as vitamin C and dietary fibre. Dry matter and, correspondingly, the starch content have a big effect on the cooking quality of potatoes. The starch is stored in grains within cells, and on cooking the starch swells up and is released. The amount of starch and the nature of this release from cells often determines the texture, being smooth or waxy to a more granular, floury sensation in the mouth. However, this general rule of thumb does not hold true for all varieties.

A high dry matter (more than 22%) is generally associated with a higher starch content. Dry matter is closely related to taste and texture. A lower dry matter (less than 20%) is typical of earlier-maturing varieties and usually (but not always) produces a smooth waxy product. A higher dry matter variety such as Maris Piper will produce a more floury baked or roast product. A high dry matter is also associated with the tendency of a potato to disintegrate on cooking, and if you are looking for a good boiling variety try to avoid the very high dry matter ones, or alternatively boil carefully, steam or microwave to reduce disintegration. Sweetness in potatoes is a characteristic associated with either immature potatoes, before all the sugar is converted into starch, or alternatively potatoes that have been stored for many months at cold temperatures where the starch is converted back into sugar, a process known as low temperature sweetening.

Potatoes may also turn grey or black when cooked, especially by boiling, and this is a consequence of naturally occurring chemicals reacting in the tuber. Some varieties do this to a greater extent than others, and wet seasons, soil type and very fertile conditions (high nitrogen) can make this worse. Another naturally occurring chemical can cause some bitterness on tasting; this is usually associated with immature or stressed potatoes. Leaving potatoes in the light may also cause this, so ensure that you store your potatoes in the dark.

The aroma of cooked potatoes is unique and often referred to as 'earthy'. This is due to a very complicated range of naturally occurring aromatic volatiles. These tend to be more predominant in immature new potatoes. Eating your potatoes as fresh as possible after lifting should be your guarantee of best flavour and aroma.

CHAPTER THREE

SEED POTATOES

Importance

Many varieties of potatoes produce small tomato-sized green-coloured berries, which have the true seed inside. Those that do not readily bear these berries may do so under seasons or situations of stress. In a garden scenario, the pollen that bears the berry may have been pollinated. Therefore, if the seed is saved and grown the following year, the variety will be a seedling of the former variety. By pollination a potentially new variety is born. Each seed from the berry that is planted may be a different expression of the former variety.

Therefore the method of producing the same variety year after year is through non-pollinated tuber multiplication. Stem cuttings can also be used, but this is normally part of the virus removal and variety cleaning rather than yearly multiplication. The health of these seed potatoes is crucial to the final crop outcome. A whole industry exists to ensure that the seed tubers are traded at the best possible health

for farmers and gardeners to grow. In this chapter we are going to have a quick look at the role of seed in potatoes for growing.

Many of the very old varieties described in this book started well but then after time failed to produce healthy and worthwhile crops. Was this due to the variety characteristics or the health of the seed from which it was grown? Was the great potato famine of 1845-50 in Ireland exacerbated by the variety's poor seed health? Aphids spread several viruses that compromise plant heath and final yield. After a few years of saving seed the tubers get weaker and more prone to many diseases, including blight.

A growing realisation that the health of the seed was critical led to the formation of a seed potato industry, dominant in Scotland, Ireland and northern parts of Britain. With the recognition that seed quality was a limiting factor in crop yield and that the cooler parts of the UK and Ireland were relatively free from aphids, a new industry developed rapidly in the 1900s. In fact, anywhere that was

A field of seed potatoes. *SASA*

remote, rugged or cooler than the rest of the country was thought to be ideal for seed production. Yet, once out in field conditions, maintaining 100% purity became a challenge. It was to be many years (the 1960s) before seed stocks could be laboratory cleaned, and not until 1970 that virus removal by stem cuttings was introduced. The absence of this technique caused the decline of many great varieties due to infected seed stocks affecting subsequent growing performance. So, to set the highest possible virus-free standard seed health starts in a laboratory. Here, tiny propagated virus-free cuttings are made that are free from any kind of infection. The cuttings are made from the very top of the infected plant and raised in a greenhouse. Later very small tubers or mini-tubers are grown outdoors but in fully protected conditions. The basis of seed multiplication has begun.

Production

In most potato-growing countries in the EU there is seed certification. This is the system whereby seed intended for marketing is subject to official control and inspection so as to provide a guarantee to the purchaser that certain minimum quality criteria have been met.

The main component of the seed potato certification scheme is the sampling and testing of land to ensure freedom from potato cyst nematodes (PCN) and wart disease. Approved seed is grown and inspected by appointed seed crop inspectors for varietal purity and crop health.

All seed potatoes originating in Britain are produced from virus-free stocks (officially tested laboratory-produced micro-plants). This ensures freedom from a wide range of quarantine and non-quarantine diseases. SASA is responsible for the initiation and maintenance of nuclear stock.

Seed multiplication and certification

Commercial multiplication of nuclear stock is from approved laboratories. Micro-plants are planted either in a pest-free and soilless substrate within a protective environment – it is essential that aphids do not come into contact with the potato plants. The initial tubers are multiplied by specialist, officially approved producers for a limited number of years before being used to produce the Basic or Certified seed that is marketed to domestic and export markets. Classification of Pre-basic and Basic seed potatoes in Britain is based on limited generations within each class, and seed potatoes intended for export will, typically, have been multiplied in the field for only three to six generations. In England and Wales, seed that meets defined purity standards can be produced without restriction on the number of generations.

At each stage of seed classification there is a quality standard that is reflected in the prices paid. Seed health is considered so important to the future of the potato that we have an industry behind all the potato-growers simply to ensure healthy seed availability. For the gardener thinking of taking seed from a healthy plant, there is a risk of virus infection.

The seed potato

Whether you are a gardener or a farmer, there is much you can do to influence your final crop by understanding how the seed crop was produced, stored, handled and managed.

Seed potatoes. *SASA*

Providing all seed purity standards are met, an earlier harvesting date of the seed crop will give correspondingly earlier growth and tuber development. This can be critical for emergence, production and eventual harvesting dates for prices in the market. This is especially important for new potato production. Tuber size is not a reflection of seed tuber health, but is important for planting rates, number of eyes and reliance of the new plant on the mother tuber should a frost occur.

Seed should be purchased or taken delivery of as soon as possible after Christmas. This puts you in control of what happens next. Examine the pack of seed potatoes and discard any rotten, sprouted or damaged tubers. I would go a bit further by washing all the tubers in warm water and discarding any with rots or large cuts. This ensures that when the tuber is planted it is as free as possible from latent infection; it will then help consistency of emergence. Sort the seed potatoes of the same size and plant in the sized groups. The best size is usually that of a hen's egg; any larger and you need to question whether the increased yield justifies the per-kilo price you are paying. Also buying seed tubers the size of baking potatoes is an odd thing as the large sizes are usually graded out and sold, so it can also be a reflection of the season, variety or skill of the seed-grower. Exercise caution with large tubers, which should not be cut, as this makes the tuber vulnerable to disease in wet conditions. However, the very small ones may not have the vigour you want and will need closer spacing. As a guide, whatever the size of the tuber, the planted weight in the row or field should be roughly the same.

Understanding seed

The role of seed in the final grown crop is critical and often misunderstood and ignored. Beyond some known key rules for seed storage, such as bright light and frost-free requirement, there is much we can do.

Sprouting is something we want to encourage. When a tuber first comes out of dormancy, it initially produces just one sprout, a condition known as apical dominance. This is due to the apical or lead eye suppressing the growth of other firm sprouts from the other eyes on the tuber. In this condition of apical dominance, the single sprout develops very quickly with all the energy of the tuber directed into its growth while other eyes remain closed.

This can be a great advantage if you want to plant the seed tuber for early production. However, the single sprout is only likely to produce a single stem,

which, despite growing very quickly, will produce fewer tubers than a seed tuber with more stems. This is a compromise between earliness and yield.

Tubers move from the apically dominant stage relatively quickly and, as the plant hormone balance changes internally, more eyes begin to sprout to form a normal 'multi-sprouted' seed tuber, ideal for planting for larger-yielding maincrop production. In most varieties, apical dominance is over by the end of January and removing the seed from cold temperatures will produce multi-sprouting. If you do find that one sprout is apical dominant, simply remove it, allowing re-growth from all the eyes.

For example, if you want a lot of small salad-size tubers you would try to manage your seed to give you lots of sprouts and potentially tuber-bearing stems. If on the other hand you want to produce baking-sized tubers, you would look to use seed with fewer sprouts and tuber-bearing stems.

Managing seed for better yield: the tricks

You can manage this process two ways. The first is a relatively new approach called managing the chronological age of the seed.

This involves planting seed, if you grow your own seed, at different dates. If you plant seed out early and grow a very mature crop, the seed will be older and tend to throw more sprouts and stems. Alternatively, planting your seed out later in the season and harvesting while plants are relatively immature will produce younger seed with fewer sprouts and stems. This is a skilful way of managing your seed to optimise your size requirements. You can employ this strategy for the particular variety you are growing. Kestrel, for example, always throws large tubers, so encourage as many sprouts as possible. King Edward tends to throw lots of small tubers, so allowing a degree of apical dominance may help increase tuber size.

Chitting

Another management tool that can be applied to your seed is what is called physiologically ageing, or good old-fashioned 'chitting'. This process involves pre-sprouting your seed before planting, and essentially gives your crop a good head start on establishing its leaf canopy, tuber bulking and advancing senescence and harvest, i.e. to give set skins for harvest. Because you sprout the seed at an earlier stage than unchitted seed, it usually means that there are fewer but more vigorously growing sprouts. It may also allow you to get your yield earlier before the blight infects your area or slugs take their toll. Chitting is a great management tactic.

Chitting to encourage short dumpy sprouts on all the eyes can de performed in a warm and light area such as a heated greenhouse. From February to mid-March you will dramatically alter the seed potato age and subsequent behaviour when planted. Place the tubers in seed trays with the rose facing upwards. Never put seed potatoes in the dark or allow long white shoots to grow.

Altering the physiological age, or chitting, seed potatoes by management is common, but there are reasons why some growers do not plant chitted seed. Usually this is to do with location and climate. Having tubers race through only to be hit by a late frost is not a good idea. Soils in the Midlands and further north may be slow to warm up, and the benefit of a chitted seed tuber is then lost. Modern automated potato planters will also damage the chitted seed potatoes.

My preference is to plant well-chitted seed in a warmed soil. In my garden in southern England, with very light soil, I know the crops will need copious amounts of water either as rain or through irrigation. This means that benefits of early moisture in May need to be maximised. It also underlines the need for organic matter to be dug in and built up. Soils in June may be warmer but, on light soil, too dry for good tuber initiation. If I plant chitted seed, plants from an early April planting will be making tubers in late May as opposed to plants from the unchitted seed making tubers in the drier month of June. The lack of water will affect the number of tubers set. What we want to achieve is the best possible environment for our crop, and that is largely achieved by good seed management.

Saving seed for the garden

If you are planning to keep some seed back, ideally the prospective plants should be protected from aphids contacting the leaves – easier said than done. Try some agricultural mesh or fleece. Spacing within the row should be close enough to prevent large tubers forming. The plant should be heavily watered at tuber initiation, which will encourage even, medium-sized tubers and the highest number possible. Harvest when the tops have fully died back, and place the progeny of each plant into an individual small pile. Select the seed tubers from the plant that has given the best yield, shape and colour of tubers consistent with the variety. Avoid selecting tubers from a plant with any kind of infection, particularly blackleg or tuber blight. Unlike other garden crops, where seed selection can, over time, create new strains or varieties, the potato progeny will not evolve and will remain true. Only by taking true pollinated seed from within the green tomato-type berries will you then create a new strain.

Virus will eventually weaken the plants and this is usually seen as leaves curling. This will eventually reduce yield. However, some varieties tolerate some degree of virus.

The practice of seed-saving should be adopted with caution and on a limited basis. Saving your own potato seed is something for the more experienced gardener and for specific reasons. Seed described as 'once grown' refers to keeping back potatoes from a certified planting and using them the following year. In warmer regions earliness of crop can be improved.

Virus in crops usually manifests itself as curled leaves; this is a virus in a Pentland Dell crop. SASA

CHAPTER FOUR

GROWING POTATOES IN THE GARDEN OR ALLOTMENT

Site selection

Potato patches usually form part of a vegetable plot within a garden or a municipal allotment. However, potatoes can be grown in any place where soil, substrate or water can be provided. For most of us, the traditional place is the soil and that is the focus of this chapter. Understanding your soil type and the appropriate management will be pivotal to long-term success.

The chosen area needs to have clean water available, in addition to natural rainfall. To get the best potatoes, or in dry weather any potatoes, water must be seen as an essential part of potato-growing. The site should be open to the light and not covered by trees, large bushes, (especially evergreens), any constant shade or affected by roots. Consideration should be given to minimising slopes to ensure an even water-holding. On sharp slopes terracing may be considered. The area chosen should be cleared of man-made waste, boulders, wires, beds, rubble, etc. Before deciding to grow potatoes, dig over a small section; this will help you identify its real history and condition. Avoid soils that have foreign matter, large stones or a crust within two spade depths. This is the most important part of the task to avoid disappointment later, so take a bit of time. Check out sites in autumn, noticing the vigour of the weeds. The more weeds the better, especially stinging nettles, as their presence indicates a level of nitrogen within the soil and their leaves can be composted.

Any location for potato-growing needs to be able to drain freely. When the spade is sunk into the soil, it should turn over the soil without it sticking. Clay soils will stick to the spade and turn over in large lumps, usually brown to orange in colour. This is a typical of a heavy soil, and this should be dug in the autumn. Further digging before the spring may be required as it is essential to get as much air into the soil bed as possible. Sand or light compost can be used when opening up the rows at planting time. Low-lying sites are not a write-off – the soil level can be raised to

enable drainage, and in seasons of drought such soils may prove very useful.

Autumn digging or spring digging

A lawn over a sandy soil should be dug when winter has passed and the weather is warm enough to trigger weed activity . Avoid weedkiller but mow the lawn as tightly as possible. Dig a trench at one end, removing the soil to a depth of two spades, then place the lawn from the next row at the bottom, covering with the next line of soil. Once finished, return the first lawn turfs and soil to line the last row.

If you are returning a lawn to cropping or taking over a disused allotment, there will be a certain amount of residual fertility. Measuring this is hard, as accurate soil analysis is beyond the means of most gardeners. Look at what is growing. If it appears strong and vigorous, the chances are you will not need to add fertility in the first year. Clover or daisies are a poor sign, indicating low nitrogen levels, while chickweed is more comfortable in soils with high organic matter and maybe light shade. While weeds can mean a variety of soil conditions, in general healthy weeds equal a healthy if not unbalanced soil.

The soil

If you want to be a really good potato-grower or gardener, or indeed farmer, the soil has to be biologically alive. This is not a new concept; this view or something like it appears in nearly every good gardening and agricultural book that I have read. Yet somehow we have forgotten this basic point. It means that the soil must contain life, some of which is seen, e.g. worms and beetles, and some unseen, e.g. fungi and bacteria. Organic matter, which is rotting pieces of vegetable material, leaves, lawn cuttings, etc, is the natural origin of all this life. Think about the weight of matter taken and how it can be returned. Soil organic matter is built by adding vegetable matter or animal manures. Apart from wooded material and evergreens, if it is degradable, compost it. Ensure a mix of material to create a range of activity and nutrient storage potential. Humus, the composted material of stalks and stems, is critical to a balanced and long-lasting material; lawn cuttings and young weeds, important as they are, will not build long-term soil organic matter. Changing the organic matter percentage of soil and its durability is a long-term process. All composted material and manures should be friable and, most importantly, free from smell or odour.

The life of the soil is dependent on the cycle of life remaining unbroken. The use of artificial nitrogen fertilisers inhibits soil bacteria; they are an acid to the delicate life, and inhibit the ability of the soil to separately fix nitrogen from organic matter. This is the key difference between an organic soil and one routinely applied with man-made nitrogen. If you want healthy soil it will not be achieved by packets of fertiliser, easy though it first appears.

The emphasis of successful gardening must be on improving the health of the soil. It should have worms, bugs, beetles and microscopic fungi, all of which aid soil friability and long-term health. Most of us are not lucky enough to be on perfect soil, so it will take time to get your soil as your crops want it. Rome was not built in a day. Let us consider what kind of soils naturally exist and the strategies you can adopt to make them great potato soils. There are five commonly known soil types, and most are a blend of several.

Sandy soil

Sandy soils have a gritty texture and are formed from weathered rocks. The particles are large and enable water to pass through quickly. The soil of coastal regions, and indeed some inland regions, may be sand-like in appearance, almost like a seaside beach. Most sands are a combination of sand and gravel. The topsoil in my garden is sand on gravel, and if you dig down far enough then increasingly it is a sandy colour with lots of small stones or shingle. Therefore my aim is to build the organic matter levels, to get body or matter into the soil. This will increase the water-holding capacity, and will also ensure that the thin layer of top soil is as efficient as possible. I like managed sandy soils; they are quick to warm up, quick to work in the spring and in most scenarios give two vegetable crops per year. I do not cultivate the soil in winter. I may put in a lightly sown mustard or even let some weeds grow. Hardy, over-wintered crops such as leeks prove very useful land cover, and have a soil-

cleansing role. Shredded leaves, compost or other mulching activity that stimulates biological activity is normally added. The golden rule is to avoid a sandy vegetable patch left open for the winter.

Compost is added to the soil several weeks prior to planting. I prefer my own compost, which at the time of application is low in nitrogen, the green waste being mixed with hay. The response from animal manure can be too dramatic and produce tall, weak plants with too much foliage, so it is used sparingly. In summer I may mulch with lawn cuttings and even more compost. All this improves the soil's 'body' and water retention. The downside of sandy soils is the high water demand, so ensure on-site water access or water storage. Their usually warmer and more fluctuating temperatures combined with high mineral content does not help skin quality for the show bench or long-term storage: the tubers will dull quickly. In the commercial world the best storing potatoes do not come from sandy soils. Very sandy soils are great for early crops and carrots, but usually have limitations for those growing to organic principles.

Silty soil

Silty soil is considered to be among the most fertile of soils, and is usually composed of fine minerals that form a balance between organic matter and aged seabed land deposits. They have a texture that is water retentive without being sticky or heavy. Silty soils have more nutrients than sandy soils and usually offer good drainage. When dry, the silt has rather a smooth texture. This type of soil structure helps to create the best balance between water, fertility retention and workability. Silty soils by their nature tend to be in low-lying drained areas, like the Fens of East Anglia, which were once great salt marshes. As the natural fertility and salinity is high, the addition of further fertilisers should be minimal. Providing the drainage and water supply can be maintained, a silty soil is a very good potato soil; crops will be of good quality and yield, and will store well. Silty soils can vary from ideal to silty sands and silty clays. Over-cultivation is to be avoided, but the addition of selective types of organic matter will be needed to keep this kind of soil in good condition.

Clay soil

At the other end of the spectrum, clay soils lack air space and water penetration. In wet weather they are sticky and take a long time to warm up; when dry they can bind together in large clods, which need to be bashed down. The potato ridges of non-irrigated clay soils split easily, allowing greening. They are also hard to work – but do not get too despondent. Clay soils can be very fertile, and locked up in the stickiness can be high levels of nutrients. They are good for cauliflowers and broccoli, which in turn are good for use in the potato rotation, so pile on the organic matter to lighten the most excessive examples of clay soils. Therefore, unlike sandy soils, clay soils will be planted much later. Less water is required, but keep clay soils free-draining. In time, you can convert this type of soil into a loam. Some really bright-coloured potatoes come from the clay and storage is usually excellent. Stones often appear in thin clay hills or downland sites and, apart from large unworkable stones or sharp flints, they should not be removed; they provide heat and essential aeration potential for this type of soil.

Loamy soil

This is the soil to which we all aspire! Considered to be the perfect soil, loamy soils are a combination of roughly 40% sand, 40% silt and 20% clay. The soil's workability is affected by its position and general drainage potential. You can group loams into variations of sandy and clay. They are usually very fertile soils full of organic matter, and can be defined as draining well, while retaining moisture. They are nutrient-rich, making them ideal for cultivation. With a loam soil, you get the best of all worlds.

Peaty soil

If you live in certain areas of the oldest parts of the Fens (and other districts) you will know all about peats. They are great soils for vegetable growing. However, there are two types. The Fens, drained from thousands of years of salinity, are perfect, but the acidic peats of the moorlands are not; here only moss, sedges or heather grow, and there is little air in the peat, which is very acidic. Choose and respect your rotations as the fertile peat soil will not last forever, inviting as it is. Peaty soil maintenance will inevitably come down to lime and water management. If allowed to become dry, a peat soil can be prone to cracking, so watering needs to be constant. Erosion can also be a problem.

In conclusion

The perfect soil does not exist – all soils will need managing to avoid them changing in structure and fertility. For most gardeners and growers the management of the soil is as important as growing. The good news is that soil will respond in a short time to efforts made to improve it, and changes will be seen in the soil and the crops grown.

Soils can be made lighter, heavier, more organic, more water-retentive and more fertile. So do not despair. With a little care and management, your soil could be a very efficient place to grow potatoes.

What type of potato?

New potatoes take less time to grow, are fantastic to eat and usually sweet. Maincrop potatoes, however, can be stored, also taste nice and help sustain you during the winter months with food you have grown yourself. By giving consideration to the planting time, variety choice and management, new potatoes could be available all year round.

An enormous selection of varieties is available for the gardener to choose from. These vary considerably in shape, size, colour and cooking and eating qualities, as well as resistance to common potato pests and diseases. In the beginning play safe and do not try every variety known to man. Ask what works in your area. Seek out the local knowledge and let that assist your selection. If, for example, Desiree works locally then start with that. Maybe buy a few tubers off others and have your own trial plot.

Each potato-growing season the soil type and method of production will yield its own vintage, which will affect the culinary performance. Assuming full plant growth is maintained, a warm summer will push up the dry matter and those varieties that usually boil without any disintegration may change and start to disintegrate. The reverse is true in wet or cool seasons. This all leads to a massive variance within any one potato variety. With time, you will get to know how a variety performs on your soil, in your area. Therein lies part of the thrill of potato-growing. Within this book hopefully resides a great potato variety for you, but it may take a few seasons to find it.

When to plant

The potato plant cannot stand frost, so there are no prizes for planting too early. Yet frost can also come quite late in the season and the grower cannot hang on forever. It is therefore a judgement call. Dates will vary from year to year and around the country. Look for the grass growing and weed activity in March/April.

Let's say, for example, that you want new potatoes. If you can protect them, you can start really early in January or February in a greenhouse, cold frame or

UK new potatoes all year round

Plant month	Harvest month	Required conditions
January	April	Heated conservatory/greenhouse, 2°C to 20°C (15°C optimum for day). Growing in a container is an option.
February	May	Heated greenhouse at night for frost prevention. Very early areas may be planted outside for late-May harvest. A fleece may be used to protect from frost.
March	June	Most southern areas can plant outside. Watch frost. Try using a fleece at an early stage until the frost risk has passed.
April	Early July	Outside. May need a fleece at early stages in northern areas. Usually fast-growing crops.
May	Mid July	Outside. Fast-growing crops.
June	Mid August	Outside. Fast-growing crops. Watch seed health and greater risk of blight.
July	September	Outside. Watch seed health and greater risk of blight.
August	Late October	Outside. Tuber numbers may start to decline from now. Think of a high tuber variety like King Edward.
September	Late November	South-facing; protect pots from frost. Always a struggle to get seed, so save from the May or June harvested crop.
September	December	Light levels falling; longer growth needed. Canopy protection required at end. Try a fleece or use the greenhouse. Use this period for the last reliable crop, which could cover low January/February supplies. Think about covering the ridge for tuber frost protection. Light levels are the biggest restriction.
October	January	Heated conservatory/greenhouse and suitable light provision may be required. Ensure a good start, but heat will be required in December for January harvest.
October	February	Heated conservatory/greenhouse, with additional light provision and expense.
November	March	Heated conservatory/greenhouse. Consider additional lighting and expense. More noticeable light in February and March.

cloche. March plantings could be under a fleece, which can be removed when the risk of frost is passed. At the small plant stage, protection from frost can be given by simply covering the foliage with earth. Newspapers can be used for larger plants. If you live in a frost pocket, keep an eye on the weather forecasts and remember the temperature values given by most forecasters are for cities, so deduct 2 or 3 degrees for rural areas. Soil is the best insulator, so ridge over if at all possible.

You can continue planting for new potatoes right up until late September, then retreat back into the protection described earlier. Winter light levels will eventually render production questionable. Thus the answer as to when to plant relates to what you want and whether the crops will grow and be protected from frost. Once again, if you look at what the neighbours

or allotment-holders are doing you will not go far wrong.

Pre-preparation and planting

Potatoes grow best in a rich fertile soil, with plenty of organic matter incorporated; ideally the soil pH should be around 6.5 or lower. Never add lime directly before planting potatoes. Lime does have an important role within the rotation and should be considered before brassica crops, especially on lighter soils, but it will raise pH levels and increase the risk of common scab. A general potato fertiliser can be added if the potato crop is part of an existing rotation and nutrients are known to be missing. On new land or land within an organically managed rotation with healthy soil, be cautious about adding fertiliser; over-fertility can cause weak, leggy plants that are prone to blight infection as well as low yields.

Start land work in the early spring a few weeks before planting. Dig over and dig in cover crops and remove winter debris. Dig to ensure that the soil bed is as friable as possible, free from all clods. The time of planting is critical: too early and the crops will not grow or be checked by frost or cold weather; too late and the seed becomes dehydrated with the elongated chits prone to infection and damage. My maincrops in central southern England are usually planted in the first few days of April and completed by the 10th. Open up a trench 1 foot deep and wide across the plot, in a straight neat line. Add the home-made compost or organic fertiliser an inch or 30mm under where the well-chitted seed tubers will be placed. Position the seed tubers rose end up in the bottom of the holes or trenches 6-8 inches (150-200mm) deep. Space earlies at intervals of 6 inches apart in the row, and the rows 24 inches apart. For second earlies and maincrop, plant spaced at intervals of 12 inches in rows 36 inches apart. Rake over the top soil to cover.

Management of your crop

Water in well, or ideally plant before rain is due. Name the variety on a stick at the end of the row and ensure you have it marked out. (Keep the packaging in which the seed came in case of emergence issues.) Do not earth up until the plants are through the ground. They can then be earthed up as they grow; this involves bringing soil up around the shoots to make a ridge. It helps control weeds, prevents the tubers turning green and gives some protection against tuber blight. Do it first when plants are around 10cm tall, leaving foliage peeping though if frost is not due. Earth up again just before the foliage meets within the rows. Plants can be mulched with a layer of leaf-mould or grass clippings. On a closer row spacing the creation of ridges is more of a challenge.

To obtain the highest yield of good-sized tubers, keep the soil moist. This is really important two to three weeks after planting, which is the time the plant is deciding how many tubers to set. Any dryness may limit setting and you will end up with fewer, larger tubers. Again, know your variety: King Edward sets dozens of tubers and less water rather than more is the rule around tuber initiation time, while Kestrel needs the encouragement of warmth and moisture to readily set tubers. This period of tuber initiation is pivotal to the final yield and quality. Sometimes natural rainfall

sorts this out for us, and sometimes we have to manage it ourselves.

Apply later watering to the soil rather than the foliage, keeping the soil moist. The plant's water requirement is often underestimated. A fast-growing plant with wide green to dark green leaves is a healthy sign. Avoid periods of slow or no growth, particularly in the period where the plants have not touched between the rows. Fast establishment of ground cover reduces weed competition, and venturing into the fully grown crop to weed is undesirable. Lack of nutrients can cause poor growth, but this is usually accompanied by a change in colour of the leaves, which can be rectified in the early stage by a foliar feed. Further lightening of the leaves is an indication of a more advanced stage of dying; this final stage is usually when the canopy has fallen.

Harvesting times

Tubers are usually the size of an egg when the plant flowers. Some varieties and growing conditions do not always encourage flowering, so look at the size of the plant and its development. In good spring conditions, the time between planting and harvest for new potatoes can be 9-12 weeks, depending on the variety and season. Again it is a judgement call. To check the state of your crop for harvesting, simply scrape away some soil at the base of the plant and look for the tubers to be the size you want.

New potatoes are best harvested as needed and cooked within minutes of being harvested to enjoy their fresh, sweet succulence. Once removed from the garden plot the young potatoes can lose vitamins and soon become tired and withered.

Maincrop varieties can be harvested for immediate use or storage. Depending on the variety, planting date and the growing conditions, these will be ready from mid-July through to early October. As the haulms die back, the skins set and become mature. When you can handle the potatoes without the skins breaking, that is the time to get them out. You could leave them in the ground and even over the winter, but the tubers will be susceptible to slugs, rodents and frosts.

Pick a nice bright day and get them out of the ground to dry. Dig up the plants by placing a potato fork to the side of the row; angle the fork under the soil base and ease up the ridge. Try to keep all the tubers harvested from each plant together, and dig the plants well, ensuring that you do not leave tubers in the ground. Leave during the day to dry before storing.

When you have finished the harvest inspect the yield from each plant and check for consistency; isolate tubers affected by pest and disease and any damaged or really scabby ones first. Estimate or weigh your yield and either pat yourself on the back or remember there is always next year!

Storing

Look carefully at any tuber with a shadow over it and if in doubt cut it. If the flesh is brown or discoloured in any way, do not store. After drying, place the tubers into a breathable paper sack. Avoid packing them wet or damp as any blight or other progressive rots may be activated. Place the sack in a shed or part of the house where light can be restricted. For winter storage ensure that the potatoes are insulated from frost. My home method is to store with minimal insulation until the first frosts are predicted, then further insulate with newspaper as required. Remove and check all the potatoes after a week of storage to see if any have become rotten, usually a sign of tuber blight, then place them back into the bag dry.

Store your potatoes in a cool, dark, airy place and protect them from frost when it is expected. Newspaper is a good insulator and light inhibitor.

Growing potatoes in containers

Growing in containers is a really flexible option and for those with limited garden access can be an easy first step; it also allows the accommodation of lots of varieties, and the inclusion of a drip irrigation system.

Potatoes grow well in plant pots or flower buckets or any object with a means to retain the soil and allow drainage. The ideal minimum size should be 35cm (15 inches) deep and 28cm (11 inches) width. Place the medium into the pot and fill to two-thirds. Plant the small egg-sized tuber about 3 inches deep. Once the plant has shown through the soil, cover progressively until the top of the container is reached. If frost is due, bring the plant indoors or cover.

Once the plant has started to flower, the nutrient within the pot will start to become strained, so, like tomatoes, start feeding once a week. This can be with a liquid potato (high potash) feed. The container method is best for growing new potatoes. The temperature and wetness will be critical in setting a high number of tubers. From one seed potato of the variety Ratte, I harvested 85 small tubers. Varieties may show increased tuber numbers from plants in containers where warmth, moisture and temperature fluctuations have combined. However, try and ensure that the daytime soil temperature is held between 15 and 20°C.

Due to the flexibility of container-growing, new potatoes can be enjoyed fresh for most of the year. The best varieties to grow in containers include the low-growing Winston, Rocket, Carlingford, Swift, Colleen, Duke of York and International Kidney (see the main variety descriptions). However, over the years, with so many varieties that needed observation for the production of this book, and fighting potato cyst nematode infections, container-growing has proved really helpful in isolating varieties, especially the dark-fleshed ones.

Potatoes for specific uses

Boiling	Salads	Mashing	Baking	Roasting	Chipping
Kestrel	Ratte	Maris Piper	King Edward	King Edward	Russet Burbank
Charlotte	Pink Fir Apple	Desiree	Red Duke of York	Maris Piper	Pentland Dell
Belle de	Belle de	Kestrel	British Queen	Rooster	Maris Piper
Fontenay	Fontenay	King Edward	Arran Victory	Desiree	Wilja
Nicola	BF15	Saxon	Dunbar Standard	Magnum	Kestrel
Wilja	Roseval	Kestrel	Yukon Gold	Bonum	Desiree
Kondor	Anya			Arran Victory	

CHAPTER FIVE

POTATO DISEASES, PESTS AND DEFECTS

Prevention

You are what you eat, and your garden will be what you feed it. Neglect it and you cannot be surprised if it takes a while to get back into condition. The first key principle is that what you remove by crop growth needs to be put back in by other crops or organic manures. Second, the health of the soil and your environment will play a large part in deterring pests and diseases entering your crops. This is the principle of the organic movement, and while the European Organic Regulation does not have the monopoly on farming or gardening wisdom, there are many great truths that apply to any kind of growing.

The things we call pests do have a right to live, but what is the point of their existence? Take slugs, for example (which we discuss in more detail later). Some slugs eat potatoes and some do not. The slug is the food of birds and hedgehogs. Kill all slugs and you potentially risk removing one part of the food chain.

In the last 20 years commercial potato production has adopted a practice called integrated crop management. This means adopting a holistic crop protection encompassing a range of strategies. For the gardener it means encouraging natural pest predators, using varieties with pest and disease resistance, ensuring certified seed potatoes, using rotations, and finally ensuring the health of the soil. It really is the only sensible way to grow food, as the chemical alternatives are so restrictive and few are confident or comfortable using them.

Potato blight (*Phytophthora infestans*)

There is a lot of mystique about blight, so here are the facts. You will only get blight in your crops if the environmental conditions are right. One key indicator of blight risk is known as the 'Smith Period', which is defined as at least two consecutive days where the minimum temperature is 10°C or above and on each day at least 11 hours when the relative humidity is greater than 90%. A 'Smith Period' is

when blight could happen. If there are spores in your area, they will multiply or even flare up from latent infections. The source of these spores could be weak, infected plants on a potato dump, discarded potatoes, or someone else's unprotected crops in the shade, where spores have erupted. Either way, black spots may appear on your potato leaves and that is the start of a blight attack.

There are two types of late blight: leaf blight and tuber blight. All varieties have varying degrees of susceptibility or resistance. It is possible, but rare, for a canopy to be blight-free while all the tubers become effected. Usually the leaf blight spores make their way to the tubers, and that is when we discuss the tuber susceptibility.

You will notice that I have not included chemical control for blight. This is because copper, the main base of the blight sprays available to gardeners, is lacking in efficacy and is also environmentally questionable. At best it has a limited effect. However, farmers have a wide range of blight sprays that are really useful and do not harm wildlife, so on this occasion the gardener remains at the mercy of the weather and is denied the armoury that commercial growers use. So much for encouraging people to grow their own food.

There is also early blight to bear in mind. As indicated in its name, this appears early in the season, and is not related to late blight. The sources are *Altenaria solani* and *Altenaria alternata*, which need a laboratory-based test to distinguish them. Plants are a higher risk when weaker or under stress within periods of high humidity. Early blight will form black patches on older leaves (late blight prefers younger leaves), and the spores will over-winter in Solanum crop debris. This disease is not currently a major UK problem, but it will become more widespread if our spring months become milder.

Right Late potato blight on leaves. SASA

Inset Potato blight in the tuber. SASA

Potato pest and disease prevention: best practice

Action	Reason
Digging	Breaks up lumps, allows unwanted stones to be removed and encourages root growth.
Digging at the right time	Spring is a great time to sort out slugs and other soil-living pests. The birds are hungry after the winter and have mating on their minds so will be looking for food. Avoid digging when too wet.
Soil aeration	Lower-lying vegetable patches can be raised by digging or by creation of raised beds to avoid drainage problems later in the season.
Maintenance	Keep paths cut and hedges low. Ensure good air flow throughout the plot.
Rotations	There are many options. Allow at least six years between varieties with no PCN resistance. If growing new potatoes and resistant varieties, shorter rotations can be considered. Include brassicas (broccoli, cabbage, cauliflower) and alliums (onions and leeks) within the rotations.
No volunteers	Remove all tubers at harvest, and as the ones you missed come up take them out. Volunteer potato plants may be weak and prone to or carry infection.
Shade	Growing potatoes near a fence, hedge or trees where light access is compromised will lead to more moisture and quicker blight infection.
Dumps	If on an allotment, look at the compost heaps of others, or in extreme circumstances piles of potatoes that have been discarded. They must be removed as they harbour infection.
Use fertiliser sparingly	Ideally this should not be needed; if it is, choose an organic-based product. Too much nitrogen leads to weak plants and a greater chance of blight attack.
Use certified seed	Start with healthy tubers with no latent infection.
Use lime	Usually before brassicas.
Diversity	Set your potato patch in the context of as many different crops as possible and the wider garden of flowering plants, over as long a period as you can.
Varieties	Start by growing what is proven to work in your local area.

Controls for minimising crop damage due to late blight include:

- Water crops in the morning
- Do not water if rain is forecast
- Do not over-manure or over-fertilise, which produces weak plants
- Clear all of last year's crop
- Encourage your fellow allotment holders/neighbours to do the same
- Ensure no dumps with discarded potatoes or potato leaves/tubers
- Grow in open areas, not under a tree or beside a fence
- Think about variety resistance
- Grow more than one variety
- Grow an early or second early multi-purpose variety
- Earth up to reduce tuber infection
- Plant wide apart (12 inches/30cm) and also in wide rows (e.g. 36 inches/91cm)
- Ensure soil is fully aerated and can drain away top surface water

Potato cyst nematodes (PCN)

This is another very serious pest that often goes unnoticed in gardens until it renders potato-growing useless. It is often referred to as the ground having potato sickness due to too many potatoes being grown in close succession on the same piece of land. Plants appear weak, short and die back quickly; the tubers are very small and there is a heavy yield penalty. PCN infections can be very localised, affecting some plants and not others. Commercially it is the number one pest in the UK and has been for the last 50 years, the result of over-cropping during and after the Second World War.

PCN is a microscopic worm that invades potato roots to feed. There are two main species, *Globodera rostochiensis* and *Globodera pallida*. In the UK *G. rostochiensis* (strain Ro 1) is the most common form.

Many older potato varieties still have no PCN resistance, but many newer varieties are resistant to *G. rostochiensis* (Ro 1), while some have partial resistance/tolerance to *Globodera pallida* (pa 2/3).

In the variety descriptions later in this book, reference is made to varieties being resistant to one strain of PCN, and this always means *G. rostochiensis* (Ro 1). For the few varieties with dual resistance or showing tolerance, this is made clear and states *Globodera pallida*.

If you have a PCN problem in your soil, cleaning it

What may be under your potato crop: PCN (*Globodera rostochiensis*) on the roots. *SASA*

up without using chemicals is entirely possible but it will take time. There may need to be a complete break from growing potatoes, but usually a combination of the control options listed below will work. Variety choice, incorporation of brassica or mustard crops, and building of organic matter are for me the key strategies. Having grown many varieties in my small plots in Hampshire and experienced PCN damage, I can now report that, with care, varieties with no PCN resistance or tolerance can now be accommodated.

In summary:

- Use a minimum six-year crop rotation
- Consider growing in buckets as part of your potato requirement with non-infected compost
- Do not grow any other Solanums, such as tomatoes, in the soil
- Use varieties with some dual resistance or tolerance to both strains
- Use earlies as a catch crop for new potatoes (pull out the plants when the tubers are young)
- Use compost and composted manure to improve the soil

How a potato crop should look. *SASA*

PCN damage in a field. *SASA*

- No-dig growing can reduce the effects of eelworm on potatoes
- Plant brassicas in the rotation and trash the leaves into the soil
- Plant mustards and dig in all the crop produced

Slugs

Slugs are probably more of an obvious nuisance to gardeners than even nematodes or blight. However, not all slugs are potato-lovers, while some love particular varieties and will bypass others to get their favourite. Variety choice is therefore important.

The most important slugs for us to worry about in order of nastiness are the keeled slug, the garden slug and the Gray field slug. The keeled slug is particularly nasty as it burrows underground and multiplies twice a year, so this is the one we really need to look out for.

Slug control in the garden is non-stop. Slugs are nocturnal, and if damp conditions persist they will thrive. One principle to be aware of is that many other species eat slugs, including beetles, frogs and hedgehogs. So once again, the importance of a diverse and active range of species should be borne in mind. Birds also like slugs, and the first dig of the year to prepare the soil is a good time to remove them. During the growing season and especially on a wet night from July onwards walking around the plot at night with a torch and physically removing slugs will help.

Keep the plot edges tidy and well cut. Remove anything overgrown that harbours a wetness/moisture under which slugs can hide. Think about the damp undersides of wood or discarded material – any place where slugs can over-winter. Slugs like heavy wet soils and the practice of digging over, especially in the spring, will dramatically reduce numbers.

Varieties susceptible to slugs: a quick check

Slugs hate	Slugs not sure about	Slugs love
Kestrel	Estima	Maris Piper
Romano	Osprey	Cara
Sante	King Edward	Marfona
Swift	Desiree	Rooster

Slug damage in tubers. *SASA*

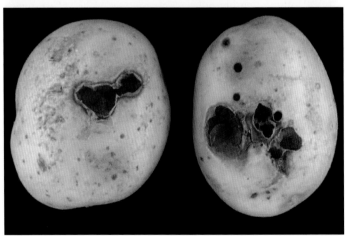

The two or three key summer months when slugs will be active – July through to September – coincide with the maincrop bulking; be aware all year round, but really go on the offensive during these three months. Applying free-living nematodes for slug control is an alternative, but start in early June before you see damage.

Although slug damage can happen at any point in the growing season, it is most severe in the autumn and in wet seasons. Pay attention to the crop development and harvest earlier rather than later.

To control slugs:

- Take steps to lighten heavy soil such as raising the level
- Dig over before planting
- Choose less susceptible varieties
- Maris Piper, Marfona and Maris Bard are particularly

susceptible to slug attack – see variety descriptions for more about resistance

- Harvest all tubers by early September if slug population is high
- Visit the garden/allotment after heavy rain and at night and remove slugs
- Put coffee slops over the edges of the potato bed, or beer traps
- Encourage hedgehogs and beetles
- Let chickens roam over the potato patch during the off-season
- Positively encourage small bird population

Blackleg

Blackleg is a bacterial infection. For years it has been known as blackleg (*Erwinia carotovora*), but is now called *Pectobacterium atrosepticum*. I still call it blackleg. It is seasonal, favouring wet conditions for development. Poor seed is usually the cause, but poor garden hygiene can also make this locally an annoying and costly problem.

Seed inspection after buying is quite challenging, as the infected tubers are likely to collapse at harvesting. However, in storage affected tubers may have a dark discoloration around the stolon end of the tuber, which might be a sign of blackleg. In all other respects, the tuber is healthy. If you detect this, do not plant the seed.

Garden hygiene should include removal of any tubers and plants with blackleg infection. All maincrop haulms should be removed and burned.

In the field, infection shows itself as odd plants with foliage looking a lighter green than others with the tops appearing curled and withered, like an aggressive virus infection. One or more of the stems may be dying, and the base of the stem may be black. On closer tuber inspection, a rot or black puncture at the tuber stolon end might be visible. Isolate infected plants and do not save the seed. Think about the source of the seed.

For commercial growers this is an avoidable problem and is usually associated with the way seed is managed. Think about the variety choice if blackleg becomes an ongoing problem. It is more probable that it will be a one-off, so do not get too discouraged. Blackleg is worse in wet seasons and can be exacerbated by over-irrigation.

Common scab

Tubers appear with raised patches, like scabs. This is a bacterial infection, which is soil-borne, so if potato seed stocks arrive with common scab on them do not panic; light tuber infections are really not a problem unless cosmetic appeal is dominant, e.g. for showing. My personal rule of thumb is that common scab is not a real problem and I rarely discard for this reason. It will be easily peeled out and will not affect eating quality; only in excessive cases might it affect storage. However, there are simple strategies you can take to minimise common scab infections, and these are:

- Choose certified seed
- Discard any that have high levels of common scab
- Follow maincrop potatoes with brassicas

Blackleg. *SASA*

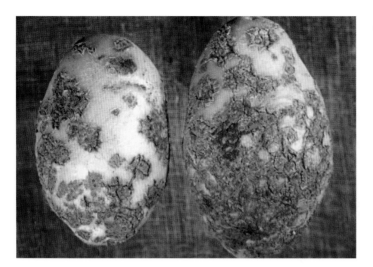

Common scab. *SASA*

- Water well at tuber initiation
- Think about organic matter levels
- Check variety resistance and susceptibility

Powdery scab

This is less prevalent than common scab, and in most cases the scabs on the tubers are not powdery scab. However, it is now an important fungal disease for commercial growers. The powdery scabs are finer than common scab and will turn to powder. Once again this is largely a cosmetic disease, so strategies to overcome it will be related to your perception of the problem. However, unlike common scab, if you are experiencing powdery scab problems you may well have other related potato pest and disease issues. The entry of the infection into the soil is not clear, but

using manure that is not well rotted is linked to this problem.

Control measures for powdery scab include longer rotations, less use of water at tuber initiation, using certified seed and, in part, varietal choice: King Edward and Desiree are useful for potential resistance to powdery scab. At a garden level measures to lighten a heavy soil would be helpful. Infection can also be confused with rhizoctonia, so a laboratory test may be required.

Silver scurf

This is another skin disease that is primarily of concern to the commercial potato industry, but not too much of an issue for the gardener unless showing is required. The key reason is the need for washing of

Powdery scab. *SASA*

tubers and their long-term storage, and the disease can form a silver lining over anything from a small patch to the whole tuber.

It is a fungus and occurs worldwide. It can adversely affect the crop's value, but is not directly related to culinary quality. Tubers in store with high levels of silver scurf can lose excessive weight and appear slightly shrivelled.

The symptoms can develop on the tuber while in the ground or during storage. Light brown to grey spots develop to a silvery 'sheen' when the tubers are washed. The fungus can penetrate a few millimetres into the tuber flesh. The inoculum is primarily soil-borne and related to soil quality/field hygiene over a long period of time.

The following practices can help reduce the development of silver scurf:

- Check seed quality
- Practice a six-year crop rotation
- Timely harvesting
- Efficient storage ventilation
- Store cold at 3°C
- Build soil organic matter

Spraing

Spraing can manifest itself in tubers as a pink to grey internal ring. There are two viruses, one transmitted by nematodes, the other, generally known as the potato mop-top virus, transmitted by the powdery scab fungus *Spongospora subterranea*.

Spraing is not often seen but can be locally annoying on light soils. Some varieties help, for example Kestrel, Avalanche and Kondor. Think about rotations and keep weeds down. With spraing, free-living nematodes spread the virus infection, which a commercial grower would send for identification.

Rots

There are several reasons why potatoes rot, the most common being blight, frost and blackleg. However, there are numerous other causes and some are notifiable (there is very useful data on the British Potato Council website and booklets).

Colorado beetle

This destructive little fellow is like a ladybird but it is striped black and yellow. If you find it report it to DEFRA.

The reason for our concerns is due to the adult Colorado beetle's insatiable appetite for potato leaves – it will simply devour a field of potatoes. It is a very

Colorado beetle. *SASA*

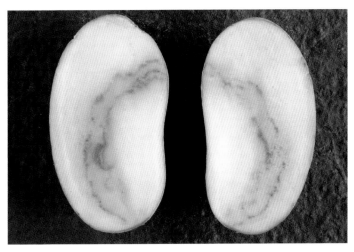

Spraing. *SASA*

Bruising. *SASA*

Hollow heart. *SASA*

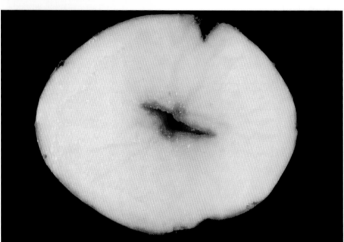

Greening. *SASA*

common pest in warm potato-growing regions including mainland Europe, but thankfully we are at present spared this pest.

Little potato disorder

From stunted or slightly stunted plants the yield is low with tiny tubers. There can be several causes: it may be frost affecting the plants, while the other rather silly cause is the planting of seed tubers that have become so aged that they are inhibited from producing a true plant.

Cracked potatoes

Harvested tubers show cracks at lifting, due to changes in growth from slow to fast and maybe too much water. The variety Rocket is prone to cracking when it grows rapidly to the larger tuber stage.

Bruising

Bruising shows itself as black or grey marks just under the skin, which may be peeled out or may descend further into the tuber. This is an important defect seen in commercial potatoes, but I have never seen it in potatoes grown in the garden. The simple cause is from dropping or knocking the tubers during harvest or movement; it is related to variety and maturity, and is accentuated in potatoes with high dry matter and during cold weather. For the commercial grower, harvesting thousands of tonnes, bruising is an absolute nightmare. Although there are many things the farmer can do to minimise bruising, it is one of the least understood factors facing modern growers.

Hollow heart

This is a separated, usually black, hollow in the potato centre, usually on large tubers. it is particularly linked to varieties (Pentland Crown and Maris Bard) and can develop when warmth follows a period of rain. Keep soil moisture levels even throughout growing season.

Greening

Greening of tubers is one of the most common forms of potato wastage. It is seasonal, being affected by both dry and wet weather conditions, and after bruising and damaged tubers is a major cause of crop loss.

The tubers illustrated will be highly toxic and therefore should be discarded, unless the crop is to be saved as seed for the next season. The type of dramatic growth of greening illustrated is caused by the tubers becoming exposed to light, usually during the growing stage. Poor preparation, ridging, soil structure and soil type are the usual causes of greening.

This common and highly wasteful problem can easily be mitigated by improved soil structure (more organic matter), ensuring deep planting to at least 6 inches (150mm), and knowing how tubers form under or away from the plant. The shape of particular varieties can influence growth greening with longer-forming varieties such as Pentland Dell and Desiree.

Ridging remains the key to avoiding greening, and at a farm level double ridging should be seriously considered. For the gardener, ridging to form even and angled sides of not more the 45 degrees is the target, with a real ridge at the top and not a sharp point. Mulching with grass cuttings and composts may also prove helpful.

CHAPTER SIX

WILSON'S TOP 100
VARIETIES

This is a compilation of my Top 100 varieties. Placed in alphabetical order, these varieties have met all or part of the following criteria:

- great culinary quality (Kestrel, International Kidney)
- outstanding agronomic features (Sarpo varieties, Cara, Kestrel)
- commercial success (Nadine, Majestic)
- historic significance (Lumper, Magnum Bonum)

I have chosen varieties that are potentially available. If they are not on the market now, by using the various seed libraries or micro propagation methods they soon could be. Some varieties are given an extra bit of recognition by the 'gold trophy' symbol, which means that they excel in all key cooking requirements expected for that type of potato.

There has been a selection process to arrive at a Top 100 involving growing particular varieties, visiting trials, and visiting over two years the reference collection at SASA (Science & Advice for Scottish Agriculture). The variety comments have been formed as part of the selection process and are based on published or unpublished data and interviews. However, a large part is based on personal experience, having worked with potatoes for more than 30 years. All of the varieties listed in this Top 100 have been personally examined as plants and tubers.

Agronomic comments are generalised, and varying soil types, locations and growing regimes may alter the presence or expression of a particular feature. The perfect potato does not exist, as variety selection is always a trade-off. For me, taste is a key driver as opposed to yield. I hope you can find at least some interesting and new information on your favourite variety.

After the Top 100 come the rest. In total, more than 400 varieties have been entered into this very personal list. However, it is by no means complete. More than 1,000 individual varieties reside in the Museum Collection of SASA, and there are many more around the world

Each variety is headed with its country of origin, date of national listing (or year of introduction as a traded potato) and its maturity grouping, e.g. first early, second early and maincrop. In some instances the terms early maincrop and late maincrop are used.

One of the key themes within this book is my affection for old varieties. The choice available to gardeners has been much improved since the first book *The Story of the Potato* was published in 1993. However, most of the pre-1980 entries are either no longer readily available or their planted seed acreage hangs on by only a small thread. If seed production ceases, the variety is placed officially into stem cutting cold storage with a few tubers for reference collections. Micro-plants and mini-tuber production has brought the potential for many more varieties to be sold, and that new development is welcomed.

ACCENT

Holland • 1991 • first early

This is a round-to-oval-shaped variety with light yellow skin and flesh. The low to medium dry matter percentage gives a firm texture, which enables the cooked potato to hold its shape. Accent can be harvested as a new potato or left to full maturity. A mature Accent can be a good all-round utility potato but there will be a yield penalty. The tubers can gain good size without becoming irregular. Accent gained considerable commercial acreage in its early years.

However, its poor resistance to tuber blight and blackleg has now reduced its popularity; the blight susceptibility issue having been overplayed. When grown as an early garden potato with less nitrogen, I have found that foliage or tuber blight is rarely an issue. It has resistance to one type of PCN, which may prove very useful if the crop is grown to maturity. Accent remains an excellent choice for those wanting real new potato flavour from a relatively modern introduction.

Accent is also a good choice in dry years, as it resists drought well. Its low, dark green, closely set foliage also makes Accent a great choice for container growing, and it is still to be found in gardens and allotments. The seed acreage is now perilously low, which is a bit of a scandal for such a lovely potato. If you want almost the taste of Duke of York, but with a modern higher yield (at least double), try Accent.

AMBO

Ireland • 1996 • maincrop

Bred from a Cara/Desiree cross, this is a cream-skinned and strikingly heavily coloured variety. It really is like the painting! This beauty of a potato variety has a slightly mealy texture and suits most cooking purposes without excelling. It is probably best used boiled or mashed, as baked tubers can be a bit moist. Fry colour is variable. Heavy yields can be expected much earlier than King Edward, whose market Ambo is rather wishfully aimed at.

The lack of effective nematode resistance could be an issue for commercial growers, but the compensation is the reasonable to good blight resistance. Spraing could be a problem, so ensure good soil quality. The final yields can be high: expect 6-7lb of good-sized tubers per plant. There is currently a significant acreage of Ambo grown. It has poor slug resistance, so harvest early as the keeled slugs will have no trouble finding this one. It is an obvious choice for the show bench, and the larger tubers hold their shape well.

ANNABELLE

Holland • 2001 • first early

A very tasty potato, it can be eaten both as new and at full maturity. The texture is very firm, waxy and consistent. The tubers have a long, elongated shape and cream skin and internal flesh. It is almost a dual-use variety as the medium-to-large-sized tubers are suitable for processing early in the season. If left for use later, beware of tuber blight as resistance is very poor. It has resistance to one strain of PCN. Annabelle is a bit fussy on soil, so ensure plenty of organic matter and water. This variety has short dormancy so stocks will sprout quickly. As the tubers are elongated, ensure good ridging to minimise greening. Annabelle is highly rated by the Royal Horticultural Society.

ANYA

This one was bred by the Scottish Crop Research Institute for Sainsbury's supermarkets in the mid-1990s. It came from a Desiree/Pink Fir Apple cross, and was targeted as a direct replacement for the legendary Pink Fir Apple. Pink Fir Apple is a very knobbly variety and can be almost cartwheel-like in shape. This was thought to be undesirable for commercial farming, causing a great deal of tuber damage. The idea was therefore to breed out the odd shape and make it straighter without losing the texture of the original. The development of Anya typified the thinking at that time that all fruits and vegetables had to be uniform, straight and true. In a sense, it was man playing God and seeking to deny the wonderful variation of nature. However, Anya did enable a marketable yield to be achieved and greater consumer accessibility without tuber breakages and damage at farm or retailer level.

If you have not heard of Pink Fir Apple (and many have not), Anya is a good-tasting, relatively high-yielding potato, and is easier to harvest than Pink Fir Apple. It is delicious eaten when cold with a salad, and has a nice balance of firm and waxy texture. We will overlook the rather weak pest and disease resistance of Anya, but it stores well, although its colour, a greyish defused pink, does fade. Ideally, stock from this variety harvested in September should be consumed by April at the latest.

Anya was something of a pioneer variety, its inception so obviously led by the supermarket requirement. It has proved popular, so well done to Sainsbury's for sticking with it when the niche volumes will never make it mainstream. Finally, of all the tubers painted for this book by the artist Caroline Bletsis, Anya was her favourite and she loved eating it.

ARRAN BANNER

Scotland • 1927 • early maincrop

Very large round tubers with deep, sometimes knotted eyes define this famous Donald Mackelvie variety, which was named after the Scottish (grand slam) Rugby Captain, John Bannerman. It achieved widespread planting in the 1930s, and during the Second World War was considered so important for the national diet that all commercial production was kept back to the following year for seed – such was the importance placed on Arran Banner's high yield capability. However, if volume is a positive boon for Arran Banner, taste must be its nadir. Before you criticise modern potato varieties for their taste, go out and eat Arran Banner; these are the potatoes our forefathers ate during the Blitz.

Arran Banner's flexible growing (good drought resistance) has enabled it to be grown around the world. Often seed was exported to such great places as Cyprus, then planted, harvested and sold back to the UK. In New Zealand in the 1960s Arran Banner still dominated the early to mid-season planting acreage. In Ireland, it was at one time second only to Kerr's Pink. During the 1940s the UK acreage of Arran Banner was only exceeded by King Edward, Majestic and Eclipse. Thereafter things deteriorated with continual decline, and today this once great variety has little, if any, UK seed acreage.

Its large spreading plants have white flowers that are rarely seen. The tubers are prone to blight and also green very quickly after harvest. Its agronomy is obviously dated but it had some blight resistance in its day.

Donald Mackelvie OBE (1867-1947) was a great potato-breeder whose varieties were all prefixed Arran from his home island. His varieties made good progress in wart resistance and yield performance.

ARRAN COMET

Scotland • 1957 • early

Bright white-fleshed tubers with good eating qualities make this one from Donald Mackelvie both interesting and pleasant to eat. It has the varieties Di Vernon and Pepo as parents, and in its day was the most widely first early grown in England. Once the mainstay of the Kent early potato trade in the Isle of Thanet and Romney Marsh, this was the new potato I grew up with in the Kentish towns of Sittingbourne and Maidstone – stocks were grown only a few miles away. I recall the freshness and the local vitality of the stocks on offer, peaking at the Whitsun festival, and a welcomed purchase after the tired and old main crop supplies in May. An important variety for Kent producers during the 1970s and '80s, in later years it was dwarfed by the Pentland Javelin.

Tubers resist drought, form early and make good size, but there is quite a size variation. The skin does tend to crack towards maturity and there may be some discoloration when cooked from later harvests. It does best on sandy soils or warmer coastal areas, and is a very good garden variety for yield and taste. It should be harvested early for best taste and also to avoid the usual pest and disease issues.

ARRAN CONSUL

Scotland • 1925 • early maincrop

This is a very good eating variety from Mackelvie. The bright, white-skinned and lemon-fleshed tubers can be rough/cracked and also a dumpy oval shape. Do not expect more than 10 medium-sized tubers per plant and prepare for a low yield. Its low and sparse foliage cover makes it risky in dry seasons. It was an important variety in its day, being commercially grown until the 1960s.

After cooking blackening was an issue, but the key positive feature of this variety is the long dormancy. It was one of Mackelvie's best offerings, but is now only found in collections.

ARRAN PILOT

Scotland • 1931 • first early

A very well-known variety, this one covered most of the England and Wales new potato acreage in the 1940 and '50s; at its peak it was only surpassed in total UK planted acreage by the maincrops Majestic and King Edward. A highly flavoured potato with a firm to waxy texture, there seems to be wide disagreement in journals about its taste. When used freshly harvested as a new potato, I think the taste is fine, but with maturity the cell structure and eating texture changes. After cooking, greying may occur, which could be attributed to the variety, soil type or type of fertiliser.

Arran Pilot is very recognisable due to its elongated white-skinned tubers, which can grow very large and misshapen if left in the ground. This variety did not fit well into the increasingly mechanised post-war potato-harvesting equipment. Taste also suffers during storage or mid-season use, so options are limited.

Arran Pilot needs warm, textbook growing conditions to obtain really bumper crops; any cold periods or growth checks will be heavily penalised. Recovery from frost is very poor. Increasingly commercial seed performed poorly and this accentuated the eventual decline, probably also due to the variety's intolerance to potato viruses. It is therefore not one for keeping the seed back for next year's planting, as next year's crops may become affected. It is still grown today by gardeners, as some really do love the taste. Arran Pilot is another very successful variety bred by Donald Mackelvie.

ARRAN VICTORY

Scotland • 1918 • late maincrop

Named to celebrate the end of the First World War, vivid purple skins on a bright white flesh adorn this fantastic pear-shaped variety. It eats like a baked chestnut. The texture is dry, reflecting the high dry matter, so do not expect Arran Victory to stay together when boiled; it will self-mash very quickly and may suffer blackening after cooking. It stores well and is best eaten late in the season. It is also a very useful exhibition variety. Arran Victory is often mistaken for Edzell Blue (and vice versa), but the latter is more of a true round as opposed to Arran Victory's pear or irregular oval.

It is a very late variety, and can produce a lot of tough, dense, jungle-like foliage with white flowers. Ensure plenty of moisture is kept in the soil around tuber initiation, and keep nitrogen levels low to manage foliage and allow the tubers to gain size. Give preference to high potash feed or fertiliser. Pest and disease resistance is poor, and white-skinned sports can occur. Remember this is a late maincrop and there should be no rush to plant. Once through the ground it will soon grow like mad in warm conditions and form tubers in late summer. The traditional harvest time is mid to late October.

Arran Victory was never popular in England and was often used as a marker variety to separate trial plots, yet it is too good for that! The Irish, always quick to recognise a quality high-dry-matter potato, maintained strong interest in Arran Victory; in Northern Ireland in 1950, 40% of all maincrop potatoes planted were Arran Victory. There is still a commercial acreage grown, so seed should be available. Waitrose and some other retailers sell this one and there is a loyal following, but you have to seek it out.

AURA

France • 1951 • second early

A silky textured, cream-skinned, yellow-fleshed gourmet potato, Aura has low to medium dry matter. However, its texture is mealy enough to contain a rich taste within the waxy tubers. These keep their shape when boiled, making Aura very good for use in salads or with a cold meal. It is not usually used for baking, roasting or chipping.

Pest and disease resistance is very poor, which has been the key handicap of this cottage-garden-type variety. Growing Aura will expose you to high blight, PCN and slug risk and more, so you have been warned. The plant is tall and erect and growth is fast. There is still some seed available today. In France it now exists only in gardens. Despite its high-maintenance growing tag, Aura deserves wider exposure. I have noticed that it has been consistently praised at horticultural shows by those wanting flavour in their potatoes.

BALLYDOON

1931 • Scotland • first early

This has an oval shape (which can be very indented), with white-skinned tubers and moderate yields. It was commercially grown in England due to its original good disease resistance. Emergence is slow, but it does catch up, and the tubers are low in number and size. So why grow it at all? The taste is really quite special, being earthy and breakable to floury in texture. A sprawling and lack-lustre plant with white flowers, it is best grown on light soils and in early regions. Ballydoon needs to be consumed as a new potato to enjoy the old-fashioned earthy flavour.

Ballydoon was popular in Northern Ireland but faded from view in the early to mid 1950s, with the last seed stocks seen in Scotland around 1959. By that time seed stock quality was poor and commercial yields had become too erratic. It was reported to be a good show bench choice and even a connoisseur's variety of the 1930s and '40s. Ballydoon originated from Ayrshire, bred by John Watson of McGill & Smith Ltd, but was replaced by the more reliable Arran Pilot. It has recently enjoyed a new lease of life as a heritage variety.

BAMBINO

Scotland • 2005 • first early

Leaving aside the trendy variety name, Bambino produces an abundance of small, pure-white-skinned tubers. It is very high yielding with more than 50 tubers per plant, and can out-perform Maris Peer by as much as 20%. If left in the ground the tuber size will only reach 40 to 60mm. It holds its texture very well like Maris Peer, which it is aimed at replacing. It has some blight resistance and resistance to one strain of PCN. It is earlier than Maris Peer and when cooked gives a consistent new-season early flavour so there is no reason why this one should not do very well.

BELLE DE FONTENAY

France • 1880 • second early

Together with the variety Ratte, Belle De Fontenay is a massive variety for taste lovers. It is more practical to grow than Ratte and gives decent-sized tubers if left in the ground. It can be low to medium yielding, but once you get to know the idiosyncrasies of Belle De Fontenay its final yields may even delight. Its tubers are a flat elongated pear shape, but misshapen when very large. It is best in sandy loam soils, does not like high amounts of nitrogen, and needs plenty of water early on to ensure high tuber numbers. The foliage is light and spreading and of medium height. It can appear weak in the field, so use the healthiest seed possible. Disease resistance is nothing to speak of and you will need a good blight plan at hand to avoid disappointment.

Yet this one is all about the long summer Mediterranean feeling of beaches, barbecues and juicy salads. You can just see the yellow waxy-textured tubers in a potato salad laced with oil and herbs. In fact, Belle De Fontenay is great for any recipe where the potato must stay together or hold its shape and colour. The larger ones can be baked, where the texture will still be waxy with a hint of natural sweetness in the taste.

Seed is hard to come by, which is a big shame. Dozens of books name this as the potato the potato-lovers grow, and high yields of small, flat, curved tubers can be expected. Unlike so many varieties that change composition in the tuber development, Belle De Fontenay will be as waxy from storage in March as lifted fresh in August. It is a popular variety in France where it proudly leads the numerous market displays of potatoes. In the UK retailers are dabbling with this special variety and it is long overdue a decent run on the retail circuit. It is certainly one to look out for, and after 130 years Belle De Fontenay is certainly enduring – a reminder that quality does, in the end, win through.

BF15

This superb yellow-fleshed potato is from Belle De Fontenay parentage, and the tuber and plant are similar in many respects to its parent. However, the flower colour of this one is white and the flower of Belle De Fontenay is a light purple. BF15 is a slightly longer potato compared with the pear or banana inclination of Belle De Fontenay, but both, if left to grow to a large size, can become shapeless.

The name BF15 relates to the variety's batch original plot number as a seedling in France, and the marketing people never changed it. It is therefore not named after the famous American B52 bomber, but

BF15 was simply the 15th plot. Neither is it a genetically modified potato, as I have been asked several times. Anyway, daft as it is, the name issue does have an influence on commercial acceptance.

Do not expect much in the way of disease and pest resistance, but do expect much from this waxy, at times mealy, variety with its light buttery and walnut flavour. If you want a strong salad potato and cannot get Ratte, choose Belle De Fontenay or BF15; the latter's culinary performance is, for me at least, as good as Belle De Fontenay. BF15 is a bit drier and has a more consistent flavour from my sandy soil in Fleet!

> The term **salad potato** relates to varieties that are excellent eaten cold or hot. Try boiling or steaming with the skin left on. They should always retain their shape when cooked. The texture can be waxy or mealy, with the best type of salad potatoes adding flavour to their great functionality.

BINTJE

This famous Dutch utility variety formed the backbone of that country's commercial acreage for most of the last century. Bred by Dutch schoolteacher and potato breeder K. L. De Vries, it was named after one of his star pupils, Bintje Jansma, who thereby unwittingly achieved a degree of immortality even before her first exam! The potato was the result of a cross made in 1904. Despite, or because of, the First World War, demand for Bintje soared, and within a few years of its release it was being grown in France, Germany and Belgium.

It was massively exported from Holland as opposed to consumed in its country of origin. The last time I saw it in UK retail outlets was in the winter following the 1976 drought. However, thousands of tonnes have been imported into this country for processing; it has for many years been the mainstay of extruded potato products such as potato waffles. It has a yellow flesh that was thought at the time to be undesirable for the British market, although that was eventually overcome by its stableness during processing.

It is good for all uses and of medium size. It excelled as a crisp and was still widely imported until the late 1990s. No real pest or disease resistance features. With the success of post-war Dutch potato-breeding, this variety has now become eclipsed. It performs well on most soils and its texture is on the waxy side. Its success opened the way to many more Dutch yellow-fleshed varieties, but although now rarely seen in the UK it is still a common variety in European countries.

A certain Monsieur Quemeneur, at his coastal home in Landunvez, Brittany, has grown personal selections of this variety for generations. I suspect he is not alone, thus guaranteeing a part of Bintje's longevity and appearance for generations of seed-savers to come.

BONTE DESIREE

Predominately a white-skinned sport from a Desiree plant, inconsistently formed splashes of pink adorn the tubers; the amount of colour varies, with many tubers having no coloration at all. The coloration/marking is aggressive, often in a straight or oddly formed patch. It is one of the few part-coloured varieties where the colour looks forced or painted on. The shape is identical to Desiree, being long, smooth and oval at medium size.

I have observed that the few crops I have grown have yielded slightly better than Desiree. The key agronomic attribute of Bonte Desiree over Desiree is maybe consistency of shape when large. Slug and drought resistance plus good storage are all the same as Desiree.

Bonte Desiree is an excellent robust variety that suits most soils. This unique sport has all the culinary attributes of Desiree, making bright yellow mash, roast and chips. It is also a very good boiled potato. It did achieve commercial acreage during the 1970s, but with the advent of washing for pre-packing, the inconsistent and aggressive colouration was seen as off-putting. In addition, the dominant success of its mother variety was well established. Bonte Desiree deserves wider acclaim and, if carefully grown to control final tuber size, would be a very distinctive variety.

Once again, a sport seems to perform differently from a variety to which it is genetically identical. This is due to the DNA of a variety being only one part of a variety's expression or character. Stress can create outward mutations that, although having genuinely different traits, contain the same DNA.

BRITISH QUEEN

A stomper of a variety! This vigorous-growing success from Archibald Findlay has won the hearts of successive generations in Ireland, where it is sold very successfully as Queens. The secret of its success lies in the high early-marketable yield, which was a key attribute in the minimisation of the effects of blight on crops. Although now well dated, it has built a strong reputation for good culinary quality. It crops fairly well and produces really nice medium-sized baked potatoes. The tubers are round with white skins, which are often crazed; this, with its rough skin and dumpy shape, makes for a scruffy appearance.

This variety is very good steamed or carefully boiled, and best consumed before Christmas as quality declines from January onwards. It has been a benchmark for flavour on both sides of the Irish Sea. It has very poor pest and disease resistance, especially to blight, and is not really suitable as a washed potato due to the heavily crazed skins.

Holidaying many years ago in the South West of Ireland during the month of August, our family was treated to some of the best potatoes I have ever tasted, harvested and cooked with a passion I had never seen. This enthusiasm and respect carried into the local shops, which placed positive promotional adverts about the variety as opposed to financial discounts. The advertisements heralded a new season's arrival by simply telling customers 'New season Queens now in stock'.

The most popular second early in the UK until the mid-1930s, it declined slowly through to the 1960s. Loss from storage was a problem for this variety and hastened commercial change in England. However, it is still widely grown all over the world, and in the UK by gardeners, and supported by some supermarkets as part of their heritage range. It still accounts for 5% of acreage in Ireland, having peaked at 25% in the 1930s.

CARA

This was originally called Oak Park Beauty after the location of the breeding centre in Ireland. I would not have changed the name myself, but Cara (Irish for 'love') is a pretty good name too! This variety throws up very large but even-sized round tubers, and on light soils they are quite tasty. It is well suited to the faster-growing soils and areas, but on heavy and poorer soils it can taste quite bland, a situation often made worse by overwatering and excessive use of chemical fertiliser or manures.

The agronomic attributes of Cara include resistance to one strain of PCN. Blight resistance is also reasonable. Cara was a marked improvement in its day on all previously introduced varieties, and is also very high-yielding, outperforming King Edward by as much as 30%. Cara has good drought resistance, and in short is a more reliable variety than King Edward. So it was no surprise that merchants during the 1980s sought Cara seed and claimed it to be King Edward. At one point it seemed that the very existence of King Edward was threatened by this malpractice, which was largely ignored.

Cara was exported to Egypt and other Mediterranean countries and sent back as new potatoes. Customers liked the bright white flesh and Cara became the backbone of the Egyptian new potato export trade. Although a robust variety and a reasonable choice for organic growers on light land, commercially Cara is losing out to other part-coloured types such as Ambo, Picasso and Vales Sovereign. To help with earliness of crops, try keeping seed back from a high-yielding plant (small egg-sized potatoes), which will encourage a slightly earlier crop the following year.

Cara remains a versatile potato suitable for a wide range of culinary uses. As a boiled potato it is firm, rarely disintegrates and holds its colour well. From the rich orange soil of Cyprus it performs well as a baking potato, but from the UK the texture is too wet for my liking.

CARLINGFORD

Northern Ireland • 1982 • second early

At Waitrose I always vote this one over Maris Peer for taste and texture. However, many people are divided. It came from the Northern Ireland state-funded breeding programme and is a cross with the very good variety Dr McIntosh. It is commercially grown as a first early, although it is really a second early maturity. It gives very high yields of small white tubers perfect for washing, pre-packing and selling in small trays, bags or loose. It was bred as a canning potato, hence the consistent, low dry matter that maintains a waxy texture throughout the season. A Carlingford lifted as a new potato in the summer will taste the same as a Carlingford eaten three or four months after the harvest, it is that stable. The only difference is that the skin is set as opposed to flaky. This attribute gives greater flexibility to the commercial grower and, unlike older varieties such as

Duke of York, the exact time of harvest can be delayed without the culinary composition of the tubers changing.

Carlingford has decent blight resistance, and yields are above those of Maris Peer. Expect at least 25 tubers of even size per plant. It has good scab resistance, but no PCN resistance. It is an accommodating variety, being responsive under polythene or fleece for early yields. It is ideal as a second cropper, forming tubers in shorter daylight conditions. It is ideal for potato salads.

It is the ultimate perfect potato and, for its intended use, just fine, but with its perfect round shape and middle-of-the-road taste, Carlingford borders on the boring at times. However, it has never dislodged its rival, the even more boring but very successful Maris Peer.

Cygnet Potato Breeders Ltd, based in Milnathort, Scotland, and Cambridge, England, acquired Plant Breeding International. The company continues to breed new varieties for the fresh and processing trade, and its varieties include Saxon, Bambino, Bonnie, Carlingford, Rocket, Cabaret, Navan, Bambino and Isle of Jura.

CATRIONA

Purple-splashed varieties have always had a rough ride from culturally defensive commercial buyers. However, purple skins were at one time more common than red and certainly commonplace in Victorian times (Skerry Blue, Fortyfold). Catriona found some serious admirers in those who loved the earthy, nutty taste. It has a creamy yellow flesh and as a second early is well worth a look by those seeking real potato taste. With its dry floury texture, it is probably one of the best varieties for baking in its skins. Use before Christmas.

The foliage is straggly and spreading but the purple flowers are abundant and very pretty. The low and mixed-sized yields are a challenge; I managed an impressive 6lb (2.72kg) yield from one plant, then less than 2lb from another in the same row. It is very prone to blight and every pest, apart from slugs, which once again seem to avoid purple skin colouration.

The amount of colour on the Catriona tubers is variable, and as a show variety it is simply not reliable – some tubers may show no coloration at all! In recent years Catriona has been sold in some supermarkets as part of their heritage/old-fashioned types, and this welcome niche market has been the lifeline for varieties like Catriona. The variety Blue Catriona (on the left in the painting) is a sport derived from Catriona (see page 130).

Catriona developed a hardcore following that kept it in modest commercial production. It was bred by the legendary Archibald Findlay, who as far as I know was not challenged over its authenticity. For more than 70 years Catriona often graced retail shelves and farm outlets, peaking with around 100 acres of Scottish seed. A small quantity of seed is still grown.

CHAMPION

Ireland • 1862 • maincrop

An historic Irish variety, Champion was the main one picked up by growers from the new selections made after the Great Irish Potato Famine. The great potato scientist and author, W. D. Davidson, recalls Champion as 'the most outstanding variety in the history of potato-growing in Ireland'. It was selected from a seedling planted by John Nichol.

This variety resisted the blight of 1879, and for several years it proved to be the single best variety in this regard; it was duly taken up by growers. In the face of limited alternatives, the acreage of Champion grew rapidly. Initially grown in and around Dublin, it soon found its way to all parts of the country. The important thing to take in here is the sheer size of this one variety's importance to a single country. After being so reliant on the variety Lumper during the 1845-50 Famine, Ireland now became reliant on another single variety. What else was there to grow successfully? Between the 1880s and the 1920s

Champion was the single most important variety in Ireland, accounting for more than 80% of all potato acreage at its peak in 1891. As late as 1917 it still accounted for 45% of all potatoes grown. Eventually it was replaced by Up To Date.

So what is this famous potato like? It is coarse to peel and the knobbly tubers are a challenge; the misshapen issue is less on very light soil and the tubers are round and more regular. In its day the odd shape was very marketable, even sought after! A round and very deep-eyed potato, it has bright yellow flesh sometimes streaked with purple. It is noted for a very floury texture and fine taste, and is best consumed the traditional Irish way, boiled or steamed in its skin. Champion produces lots of small-sized tubers, and is a very late maturing variety that stores well. Tubers have a long dormancy, making Champion ideal for use at the end of the winter and spring.

CHARLOTTE

The famous and popular Charlotte is planted all over the world, and is a variety for those who seek the summer Mediterranean feeling. It has the close texture of a good salad potato with the size and overall performance of traditional types. It is also a very flexible variety, being suitable for all culinary purposes. You do not often hear people rave about potatoes, but I have heard plenty align themselves to Charlotte. It can be baked, and can be eaten as very small tubers, where the texture is close and waxy. Larger and more developed tubers offer a lighter feel but still retain the sweet taste. Charlotte is best used before Christmas.

Charlotte tubers are elongated and flattish, although larger tubers may show a hook at the heel end. The skin and flesh colour is yellow. It produces good yields with high numbers of uniform, smooth-skinned tubers. In order to manipulate size, try spacing the seed more closely between and in the rows to encourage production of medium-sized tubers. Water well and you will be rewarded with a very large yield indeed.

Charlotte has poor resistance to foliage blight and only slightly better with tuber blight. There is little if any PCN resistance, so overall quite poor agronomy. Good slug and common scab resistance help minimise tuber waste. The plant is close-leafed, vigorous and makes a full canopy quickly, with lots of stems. The flowers are a pretty, faint purple, which helps makes it an attractive plant to grow.

Charlotte is sold in most UK supermarkets, and is very common in the supermarkets of France, where it has replaced Belle De Fontenay. In the South of England Charlotte is one of the most popular choices for gardeners.

CONGO

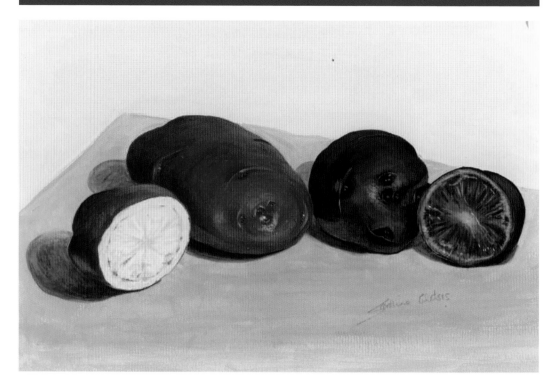

Its round black/purple skins with purple flesh make Congo (on the right in the painting, with Cardinal on the left – see page 131) a striking variety. Although new to today's gardeners, the concept of coloured-flesh potatoes was, and still is, common in Peru, the home of the potato. In Andean civilisations these pigmented types were used to make dye and also used in religious ceremonies.

Congo has deep eyes and a prolific amount of small tubers – you will be digging them up for years! After one gets over the excitement of the black/purple flesh, it is really quite ordinary in taste when boiled – in fact,

inedible is the word I should use. The texture is crumbly/breakable and it does not hold its colour when cooked. However, as a baked potato Congo is more palatable.

Disease and pest resistance is very low. The foliage has light green leaves with black stems, which makes for interesting discussion and a different type of plant to look at. It is best grown on strong moisture-retentive soils to stand any chance of a good yield and adequate culinary performance I am reliably informed that Congo has the same DNA as Vitelotte.

CRAIGS ROYAL

Scotland • 1947 • second early

This is one of the early varieties bred and introduced to the market by the Scottish Plant Breeding Station. It became very popular variety in England, as it was an early bulker, setting tubers in number and good size well before other varieties. It was so successful in this regard that its stock was often used as a first early in some districts. This attractive part-red variety (on the left of the painting, with Dunbar Cavalier on the right – see page 136) has a diffused red coloration in varying amounts, sometimes hardly at all. It is a close-textured potato with excellent culinary qualities for all cooking purposes, offset by limited disease and pest resistance.

It shows hairline cracking on the skin, and is a tender potato and not really suited to the rough mechanical commercial harvesters of the 1950s. After being the most popular second early variety in England, Craigs Royal declined sharply in the 1970s, with only 1 acre of seed being left in Scotland by 1980.

In 1957 J. Marshall of Dunning, Perthshire, introduced the all-red variant called Red Craigs Royal (see page 149), which replaced the original and was even more popular.

CULTRA

Ireland • 1988 • early maincrop

This is a Desiree/Cara cross with a leaning to Cara more than Desiree. It is a high-yielding variety with low outgrade levels, very dense foliage, long oval tubers, parti-coloured skin, cream flesh and distinct, spreading pink eyes. It has good overall disease resistance, including resistance to one strain of PCN. It also has excellent cooking characteristics, with long-term storage potential, but could be prone to internal rust spotting.

DESIREE

One of the most important varieties in terms of impact, acreage gained and culinary quality, for many years Desiree had the largest UK acreage, beating Maris Piper. Like King Edward, it has fought off many pretenders to the pink/red-skinned market, and is still with us, well-known and much loved. It was a pioneer variety from Holland, one of the first of an avalanche of Dutch introductions that still today shows no sign of let-up. At the time if its introduction Desiree improved total yields for growers, while its ability to be ready for harvest a few weeks earlier than other comparable types was another key factor in its success. It can grow on almost any soil and positively thrives in the shallow clay soils of Kent, Sussex and Hampshire.

Desiree is a very robust variety tolerating all kinds of conditions including light frost. The large, dark-green plants produced are early bulking with high yields. Its agronomic features are dated, and if you are worried about blight you may have to pass over it. There is some resistance to slug damage and common scab, but no PCN resistance, while resistance to drought and powdery scab is good. Desiree has a medium dry matter level, which produces a firm texture sometimes described as slightly waxy to mealy.

The culinary quality is excellent. It boils superbly, bakes/roasts well and is an inspired choice for home chip-making. It is one you can trust and beautiful to grow, with lots of purple flowers that readily set berries. When growing Desiree, ensure that the crops do not get too big as the tubers can become misshapen. It remains one of the best post-war introductions for taste and yield.

Its position as the most common fresh-use pink/red-skinned variety has been challenged by Romano, and more recently Rooster, which are very different types of potato. Acreage of Desiree is in decline, but there are still plenty of crops around, and I predict that it will be with us for many years to come. It is a known, hardy, reliable and well-liked variety, and a favourite of Delia Smith. Need I say more!

DI VERNON

Scotland • 1922 • first early

How this one has not ended up on someone's hot list I do not know! It is a fantastic variety. It has a bright, close-spotted, purple-splashed skin, mostly at the rose end. About one in 20 tubers have no purple marks at all or can be so faint as to deceive. Tubers are a smooth kidney shape, and the flesh is bright white holding its shape and colour well when cooked. It has a close texture and at early lifts a sweet taste. It is a variety that needs to be eaten early, so do not allow the tubers to make a size beyond that of a hen's egg. The taste does become much less prominent at later lifts and the texture becomes soapy.

This tiny piece of history was bred by the legendary Archibald Findlay, whose name as a Victorian/Edwardian leading breeder crops up several times in this book. It is a true gardener's potato, while commercial acreage was modest and mainly encouraged by the variety's ability to be very early for harvesting; acreage was restricted to Cornwall. By the 1940s Di Vernon was listed in most recommendations to gardeners but seed production ended in the 1950s.

Di Vernon has low foliage cover and its growth is very fast for a first early. It is a good choice for greenhouses, cloches or pot-growing, and in such environments the yield will be good from warm and moist soil. It is one for the light early soils of the South and South West. On the downside the agronomy is poor and the yield is light, but can be improved where warmth can be assured. The very low foliage cover often reported in history books and seen by the author could be related to seed quality; if virus-free seed was available, top growth might be heavier.

DUKE OF YORK

This is my personal favourite new potato, and is simply as delicious today as it must have been more than 100 years ago when it was released. Bred by W. Sim of Aberdeenshire from an Early Primrose/King Kidney cross, it modest but fanatical following ensured a low but commercial acreage planted throughout the 20th century.

The tubers are light yellow and oval-shaped, sometimes tending to resemble a pear. The foliage is relatively low and recovers from frost well. Duke of York is very good for growing in container, cloche or greenhouse, and to catch its sweet summer scent harvest the tubers when young and the size of a hen's egg. The foliage will be dark green, sporting white flowers. Yields are on the light side but comparable to most old varieties.

Its culinary strength is also its limitation, as the tubers do rapidly gather dry matter. If left too long in the ground, the rich, fresh sweet taste and close texture give way to a chestnut flavour and a floury mealy texture. This makes it a high-dry-matter variety, which readily breaks down when boiled; later lifts are therefore great baked or roasted. If you are planning to use when mature, then grow as with maincrop spacing.

On my light soils Duke of York has been my first choice first early for many years and, despite its poor agronomy, I have not encountered a problem. The trick is to get the potatoes in and out quickly. The yield can be low and tubers sometimes scabby, but respectable in all ways. Size is variable.

Waitrose has sold this variety consistently each summer since the early 1990s, and was one of the first old varieties to make a comeback through the raised awareness of potato varieties. The earliest stocks are grown on the Suffolk coastline east of Ipswich.

DUNBAR ROVER

Scotland • 1936 • second early

This variety was bred by Charles Spence of Dunbar, East Lothian, who only released five varieties, but all were of good overall quality. Dunbar Rover represented the culinary quality end of the second earlies of the day, winning the Lord Derby Gold Medal in 1937.

The smooth, creamy-white skins with fairly deep eyes are prone to crazing, and this variety is best grown on light soils to bring out the fresh floury texture. The tubers are of a reasonable even size but struggle to make an impressive baker percentage. Yields in variety trials dating back to the 1930s were impressive, but in commercial production these were not realised, the final yield being lower than its chief rivals, British Queen and Arran Banner. This was the key factor in Dunbar Rover not becoming well-established as a commercial variety. By the 1950s its acreage was all but limited to garden trade, and it has held this position; however, with the revival of interest in old varieties Dunbar Rover seed can still be found today.

It is in the kitchen that Dunbar Rover really excels. Its high dry matter, especially on light soil, makes the tubers perform well with a floury texture. They are therefore excellent for mashing, roasting and baking. Like the famous King Edward, Dunbar Rover has a distinctive, recognisable taste for which it has built up a cult following in the heritage potato market.

The agronomy is dated, but virus resistance is useful. The earliness of marketable yield is helpful for avoiding blight. The plant has a strong dark-green habit of medium size that is easy to manage, and the tubers store well. Charles Spence did not use any manures when testing his varieties, so the use of artificial fertilisers or organic manures should be minimised or avoided. All of Spence's varieties can produce too much top growth at the expense of tuber production.

DUNBAR STANDARD

Scotland • 1936 • late maincrop

Here is another Lord Derby Gold Medal winner from Charles Spence, bred and raised on the heavy red East Lothian soils of Dunbar. This late and very vigorous variety will grow 6 feet of haulm and have little or nothing underneath; this is because it does not like nitrogen or bulking in the long summer days. It is in every way a late maincrop potato, so you have been warned! It tends to perform best on the soils that replicate its origin; however, get the nutrition right and Dunbar Standard is a very interesting variety.

Dunbar Standard throws very tasty and large tubers for mid-winter use, the shape being oval to long oval; the flesh and skin are creamy white, which can discolour after cooking. Dunbar Standard is good for all cooking purposes, but I like it as a mashing or baking potato, where I can pick up the fantastic chestnut flavour. It is a very good keeper. Although the variety's dormancy is the same as King Edward, I find the tubers keep longer, enabling them to be used well into April. If I had better and heavier soil, I would grow Dunbar Standard more often.

Commercial acreage was significant in the 1940s, and a small quantity was grown in the red soils of Devon and the North of England. Dunbar Standard is still grown commercially today as a heritage variety and is too good to disappear. It was once rated as a decent show bench variety, but is perhaps not one to try if you are just starting out.

Charles T. Spence was a private potato breeder based in East Lothian. He did not use manure on his crops, which were raised at 1,000 feet above sea level. Spence launched five varieties, all prefixed Dunbar: Archer, Cavalier, Rover, Standard and Yeoman.

EDGECOTE PURPLE

England • 1916 • second early

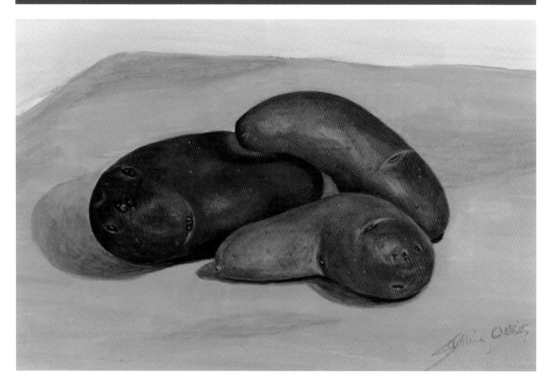

Highly rated in culinary terms, this distinctive, elongated, purple-skinned, pale yellow-fleshed potato (on the left in the painting, with Kepplestone Kidney – see page 141) has a close texture and great flavour, very different from the floury Edzell Blue and Arran Victory. It was never a mainstream variety, but pops up now and then in villages and in die-hard potato-lovers' collections.

The plant has a vigorous sprawling variety, is fairly open in habit and is quite attractive, being heavily pigmented. Skin colour can be patchy and netted. There were lots of small tubers on the small number of plants I have grown, but on better soil this variety would be capable of some interesting yields with good-sized tubers. It is certainly interesting to grow and one that deserves wider attention.

EDZELL BLUE

Scotland • 1890 • second early

Edzell Blue was the first purple variety I ever saw. I am not sure about its taste, but it is certainly more floury than Arran Victory and for me lacks the flavour and scent. One to debate perhaps?

Edzell Blue tubers are a dumpy oval, rather flat and indented at the heel end. The eyes can be dramatically deep and enveloped. The striking purple-coloured skin gives way to a snow-white flesh, which when cooked has a very floury texture, and readily breaks down.

The foliage has light-green leaves with a hint of blue pigmentation. It is spreading, almost weak in appearance and lacking vigour. However, it is quick to form tubers and an early marketable crop. It is one of the few varieties to be immune to wart disease, which was topical around the time of its release; this made Edzell Blue of some importance to breeders in the early 20th century. Its main use has been in separating trial plots by tuber colour. Edzell Blue pops up all over the world in collections.

Donald Mackelvie (1867-1947) was a private breeder based in the Isle of Lamlash, and was responsible for the all the varieties prefixed Arran. These amounted in total to 17 introductions, with many becoming household names such as Banner, Chief, Consul, Comet and the magnificent Arran Victory. His varieties were introduced before plant breeders rights were established, so he never profited from his work.

EPICURE

Bred by independent breeder James Clark from Christchurch, Hampshire, and introduced via Sutton's, this is arguably his most famous and enduring entry. It is still grown in Ayrshire, Scotland, which tells you something about the quality and the people. The Scottish palate tends to prefer a potato of substance, and Epicure is just that. It is a hardy plant, recovering from frost well. The dark-green foliage produces white flowers and, after they have fallen, a reasonable crop. It likes growing in challenging, cool conditions, producing round, fairly deep-eyed tubers, with a white skin that can show a faint red blush.

The bulking is early and the tuber size can be large to very large. Epicure is prone to most potato pests and diseases, but the slugs avoid this one, which is great. The haulm is vigorous and spreading.

Once Epicure was one of Britain's major early varieties, with 50% of the acreage being grown in Scotland. It was replaced by Arran Pilot and Home Guard in England and Wales, but kept substantial acreage throughout the 20th century. In recent years Epicure has made something of a comeback within the garden trade.

James Clark (1825-90) was a Victorian botanist and potato variety breeder based in Christchurch, Hampshire. He used Early Rose and Victoria as parents, and his varieties included the successful Magnum Bonum (1876), Abundance (1886), Ninetyfold (1897), Epicure (1897) and the forerunner of Golden Wonder, Maincrop (1876).

ESTIMA

Holland • 1973 • second early

Estima was widely used as the standard white variety in British supermarkets soon after its introduction, and is currently second to Maris Piper as the most extensively grown variety in the UK, a position it has held consistently for 25 years, although this now shows signs of decline. The commercial success of Estima was in part attributed to the challenges in growing Maris Piper, which is very soil specific. Herefordshire adopted Estima, which produced very large yields on fresh soils that had not grown potatoes before. The earliness of harvest was also decisive, together with its suitability for long-term storage.

Tubers can be large and hold their shape well. The skin and flesh colour is cream, and as a washed potato Estima performed well, with good resistance to growth cracks and secondary growth. It can be susceptible to blackleg, so always choose reputable seed-sellers and perhaps do not save your own seed. The plant is compact and has white flowers. On land where potatoes have been grown for many years, yields will be compromised. Due to the massive acreage of Estima, you have almost certainly eaten it and, if travelling around the UK, seen it growing.

A functional potato with low to medium dry matter that retains its shape well when boiled, it is suitable for all culinary uses. Its main rival in the 1970s and '80s was Wilja, but Estima is better in shape and appearance. However, it is easily beaten on taste. If ever there was a farmer's potato, then Estima was it, and it remains one of the most successful introductions of the last 50 years. I am not sure what the commercial world would have grown if Estima had not been introduced.

FLOURBALL

Marketed by Sutton's Seeds, this large red-skinned potato has very pleasant eating qualities. It was said to have some resistance to blight at the time of its introduction, but this claim soon faded. It was a common variety with Victorian gardeners and farmers, and there seem to be many imitations. The Sutton's Seeds catalogue of 1877 reports:

'The splendid cooking qualities of the red skin late in the spring when all other varieties are worthless, alone places it in the first rank as one of the most valuable potatoes ever sent out.'

In addition, Flourball was taken to Australia in 1872 and was reported as follows:

'…Messrs Fidler & Webb imported from England a few pounds of a new variety of potato named "Sutton's red skin Flourball" and it was said that it had proved to be free from disease, kept well and had splendid cooking qualities, and in the 1874 season it proved to be an excellent cropper.'

Flourball is very prone to late blight, so be warned! It is comparable to Red Duke of York in eating quality. Tubers can become very large and the yield very good, if you escape the blight. There was said to be a white, or part white/red-skinned Flourball, which preceded this red version.

A variety also named Flourball was introduced in 1895 by Sutton's. This appeared to be separate and distinct from the original Flourball described here, but it has the same colour skin, maturity and seems to have much in common.

FOREMOST

One of the last varieties bred/released by Sutton's when based in Reading, England, Foremost has Epicure in its parentage. A very good early variety, it holds well in the ground during June and July and is a really nice eating potato, offering a bright white flesh. Simply put, it is a very good choice for the early areas. The medium to large-sized tubers have good oval shape and shallow eyes, and the yield is good with mixed sizes.

I really like this one, but it never took off commercially. Foremost does need a good start and responds well to warm locations. My very early plantings are in an unheated greenhouse. It does not like cold or stressful conditions, which can induce a condition called little potato syndrome, where several very small tubers form close to or on the stolons, and can taste bitter. That alone could compromise this variety in some seasons.

The plant is quick to emerge and has a part-open habit, which can appear spindly later in the growing season. The bright white flowers sit on medium-green foliage with large leaves that are short in formation. This variety has low resistance to blight, so harvest promptly. I find the stock a little slower to emerge than other earlies and, as a plant, quite straggly and short.

Precious little stock is still grown, and it would be very disappointing if this one was lost from view.

> **Sutton's Seeds** played a major role in bringing new potato varieties to the market in the second half of the 19th century. The company's catalogue of 1877 listed 66 types, with many American imports; some were prefixed with the Sutton's name. Martin Hope Sutton (1815-1901) was the driving force. The company still operates in the garden seed potato market.

FORTYFOLD

Unknown • c1836 • maincrop

One of the oldest potato varieties still around, Fortyfold has a striking purple skin flecked with yellow, a very true round shape and a buttery eating texture. Described by the Sutton's Seeds catalogue of 1877 as 'a first rate old variety', it was mentioned in Lawson's Agricultural Manual of 1836, hence the date given above. However, Lawson describes 'Taylors Forti-fold' as 'oval much flattened dullish red in colour. Mealy, super flavour and healthy.' This description is very similar to the potato we know as Fortyfold, so we can presume that by 1836 it was already around, and had been established prior to this date. The prefix 'Taylor's' refers to the man who first marketed the variety in the Lancashire area.

The eating quality is unique, being very buttery if harvested when the canopy is at the part dieback stage. Those fully mature can be drier in texture but the lovely flavour and aroma remains. Tubers are medium in size but plentiful. Due to the dullish purple coloration it is hard to ensure that all have been harvested, so look out for volunteer plants the next season; this is a real problem commercially. The plants are vigorous; try container-growing to ensure tuber segregation.

Fortyfold is sold by Waitrose as part of its heritage range, and seed is available through specialist seed merchants.

Lawson's Agricultural Manual published in 1836 is a great piece of Victorian botanical recording. It includes a list of 146 potato varieties with interesting descriptions. Lawson described each variety's botanical and tuber features as well as starch levels – a truly amazing piece of work.

GOLDEN WONDER Scotland • 1906 • late maincrop

I do warm to this one as it has bags of character. It has a predominately russet skin, and an oblong shape. It is a hard, coarse potato, stubborn to yield and obtain a large tuber size. It is a dry floury type with a fusion of flavours from chestnut to almond. A dry matter of around 24% is usual and, of course, I wonder where the Golden Wonder crisp brand got its name from…

It has good resistance to dry rot, skin spot and common scab, but no PCN or blight resistance to speak of. The tops can grow and grow, so keep fertiliser application low and top-dress with a foliar feed during the season. Ensure that you plant seed of a decent size (large hen's egg) and that the seed is well chitted. Do not plant too early, as this one needs a long, unbroken run up to the summer yielding season. Golden Wonder will be one of the last crops to harvest, so the tops have to be in good condition for a long time. There are easier potatoes to grow than Golden Wonder, but it was very popular as a late season potato in Ireland throughout the last century and is still widely grown today, although acreage is fading.

GREAT SCOT Scotland • 1909 • second early

B red by E. Miles of Mickeholm and raised by G. Mair of Lockerbie, and intended as a replacement for the variety Up To Date, this successful introduction offered reasonable disease resistance in its day and an earlier harvesting window. It also cropped well. The tubers were often large with round, rough, white skins and deep eyes. Considered to have reasonable flavour when used straight from the field, it was very popular in Scotland and held ground for 50 years as the UK's most popular second early potato. Today the agronomy is very dated and this tall variety is rarely seen.

HARMONY Scotland • 1998 • second early

A nother successful variety bred by Jack Dunnett, it has shiny white skin and flesh. With a parentage of Nadine and Stroma, one should not be too surprised by the culinary outcome or the commercial success. This is a modern potato bred for the modern low-cost industrial growing and storing world. It is ideally suited to the UK washing market, giving very high yields of bold bright tubers with low levels of outgrades. It has very good agronomy, including dual PCN resistance/tolerance to both strains, especially G. *pallida*. It has excellent storage characteristics with long natural dormancy. The eating quality is good for boiling, but less so for roasting, baking and chipping. It has a high demand for water.

HIGHLAND BURGUNDY RED

Scotland • 19th century? • maincrop

This one came out of the woodwork during the 1990s, seen at the Potato Days held at the Henry Doubleday Research Association (now called Garden Organic). It is not a new variety, being identical to the variety Red Salad Potato, but is much older and almost certainly dates back to Victorian times. Tuber manifestation seems different and unique, consistent with what happens when someone selects their own seed and retains the stock year after year, thereby creating their own strain.

As seen in the painting, the variety is consistently bright, with a beetroot blood-red flesh. The outer ring of the tuber is usually white, but apart from that it is red all the way through – very stunning and definitely getting the conversation going at horticultural meetings.

From clean and strong seed this variety is a heavy yielder and the individual tuber size can become large,

but usually overall size is small. The plants are sprawling and of course prone to all diseases, although no more so than most old types. This variety needs plenty of regular water supply. It is an attractive plant to grow: the leaves are a shiny lime green with contrasting beetroot-like red stems, the colour of which extends to the leaf base. The plants can be tall.

The cooked appearance is a diluted pink and in no way stunning or striking. The high dry matter makes this variety suitable for baking, roasting and processing. It is not suitable for boiling due to breakdown within the cooking process. It is a novelty variety that has made it to the shelves of leading supermarkets and also processed as crisps. Its contribution to the advancement of potato varieties cannot be ignored, and at least we, the people, know that varieties like this exist.

HOME GUARD

Scotland • 1942 • first early

This variety was first entered into local seedling trials in 1937, but withdrawn owing to its weak foliage. A certain Mr J. Gladstone persuaded McGill & Smith to revise this decision and Home Guard was launched in 1942. It gained acreage on the back of its name and wartime desperation for food.

It is an early variety and its earliness of yield was a key feature. It is earlier than Arran Pilot in both Pembroke and Cornwall and this helped its adoption there. Eaten fresh from the ground and young it is fine, but Home Guard quickly develops blackening after cooking, a condition that can be exacerbated by heavy application of organic or inorganic nitrogen and also wet seasons. It produces short oval tubers with white to cream flesh, but is not a strong tasting variety.

Home Guard is a heavy cropper that needs consistent moisture around the plant for the very best results. Management of the seed was always a challenge as Home Guard breaks dormancy quickly and forms robust sprouts, but at the expense of mother tuber vigour.

It was very popular commercially in Pembrokeshire up until the end of last century, and plenty of seed is still grown, so it does endure.

> **McGill & Smith** is a Scottish-based potato marketing company with many varieties to its credit. In the mid-20th century it released many important varieties, including Doon Star, Gladstone, Ballydoon, Home Guard and many more. The main breeder was John Watson from Ayrshire.

INTERNATIONAL KIDNEY

England • 1876 • second early

This variety was bred by Robert Fenn of Sulhamstead, near Reading, and brought to the market by Alex Dean. Dean was most impressed, as he wrote in *The Garden Magazine* in 1876:

'This variety has well maintained its character as the best and most productive of all white kidneys. It is one of Mr Fenn's recently raised seedlings and is the production of a cross between Early White Kidney and Dawes Matchless. Those who saw the fine samples it produced last year will not soon forget it. And although the season has been a bad one … it will be found in fine form again this year.'

Fenn was multiplying stocks in 1875 and the first quantity of commercial seed was released to gardeners the following year. Fenn dedicated its name to the forthcoming and legendary international potato exhibitions. It was immediately recognised as having a fantastic kidney shape and a clean skin, and was one of the most popular potato varieties on display in 1878, with 20 dishes! I am therefore compelled to revise the date of introduction from 1879 to 1876, the year that the first marketable seed was offered.

It has a perfect kidney shape, an absolutely delicious taste when young, and one of the strongest scents of any potato variety when cooked. At maturity, International Kidney retains a close texture with some moderate disintegration. Stock is also canned, and mature tubers are even made into crisps. Quickly selected by growers on the island of Jersey, it became the mainstay of the island's highly successful export business, and each year the island has shipped around 30-50,000 tonnes in April and May, all to the UK. International Kidney became known as Jersey Royal, which is the sole potato variety protected by EU law that designates Jersey as the only place where it can be commercially grown.

The plants are medium to tall in height, very erect with dark-green mottled leaves and white flowers. The roots are deep and the plants appear very robust, but the agronomy is poor. For planting, purchase true International Kidney seed and enjoy the best new potatoes of the season or, if buying, choose Jersey Royals.

KERR'S PINK

Scotland • 1917 • late maincrop

From a Fortyfold cross came this monster of a variety, bred by James Henry and named after William Kerr, the merchant who introduced it.

The round tubers are a defused pink, stronger at the rose end, and the flesh is a creamy white. Plants are sprawling with many white flowers. It has very poor agronomy and is also prone to second growth. The foliage is very dense, tall and vigorous. When grown in the South of England the stored tubers break dormancy early. Kerr's Pink likes the rugged and cool climate of Scotland and Ireland, where it made its name. It has a high dry matter, which gives it a mealy but strong taste; avoid boiling it, but steam gently for the very best aroma and flavour. It also excels as a baked potato. If you like large tubers, plant this one a bit wider in the rows.

How refreshing it was to travel to Ireland and see shops with signs advertising 'Kerr's Pink now in stock'. It has been one of the three dominant varieties for most of the last century (with Queens and Golden Wonder), and today it is Ireland's second most popular potato, with Rooster first. At its peak in the middle of the last century it was also the most popular variety planted in Scotland. It is one of the few potato varieties to be instantly recognised, even sought after, and that is some achievement for a variety closing in on its 100th birthday. It is still offered by UK seed suppliers.

KESTREL

Probably the best potato variety to be introduced since the Second World War, this predominately white potato with purple splashes is, in my view, potato-breeder Jack Dunnett's best-ever potato variety. It was a pioneer variety when introduced, combining unusual skin coloration, excellent agronomy, fantastic taste and universal culinary performance – and that really does mean good for all culinary purposes. Kestrel can chip, boil, bake, roast and steam, and usually stays together when boiled to make a nice potato salad, with a fresh, almost new potato taste even in mid-winter. It is best eaten from harvest through to February, and the cooked tubers remain a bright white colour.

Kestrel has good resistance to the golden (G. *rostochiensis*) PCN and partial to the white (G. *pallida*) strain of nematodes. This dual effect is still rare today, and when released in 1992 only Sante boasted the same kind of claim. Resistance to slugs is high and it also shows some tolerance to drought. The only chink in its agronomic armour is the low late blight resistance. Low tuber numbers are a problem, so ensure that the plant is well watered at tuber initiation time, which is three to four weeks after emergence. Average tuber size is good and there are few undersized outgrades. But beware – this variety can grow very large tubers.

UK acreage is fairly low with most seed stocks being used for Waitrose or the garden trade, although it has made good progress on the worldwide stage. It is one of the few varieties truly bred for gardeners, the potatoes offering consistently good yields of large tubers. I currently grow Kestrel as the main potato in my garden, and it is a great variety for both new and experienced growers. I receive many positive comments when Kestrel is served.

KING EDWARD

England • 1902 • maincrop

How fitting that Kestrel should appear alphabetically next to the most famous British potato of all time: King Edward. This is a high-quality potato that everyone knows. Originally called Fellside Hero, the very first stocks were passed around a bit before John Butler released it as King Edward. Its culinary quality is great, but boiling may be a bit tricky. I like to use it early in the season as a second early while the tops are dying back and the skins almost set. The aroma is powerful and the taste sweet and delicious.

King Edward has been the benchmark for quality for more than 100 years, although it is a bit of a challenge to grow due to its outdated agronomy. It needs a deep, moist and fairly strong soil to get the best yields, and a foliar feed is often required. It naturally throws an abundance of tubers, which require plenty of fertility to ensure that they make size. Today nearly all the commercial crops are grown in East Anglia. The foliage has distinctively strong, closely knitted leaves with a slightly higher green than many others; flowers are rare. King Edward almost needs royal treatment, not liking stress or drought or even under-watering; apart from reducing yield these encourage the plant to form misshapen tubers. Stress during the growing season will also encourage maturity and, once harvested, the tubers will break dormancy earlier.

King Edward has fought off many pretenders to its crown, including Gladstone, Cara and plenty more parti-coloured varieties. After the 1976 drought King Edward acreage really tumbled, as it does need water. Currently, Ambo sometimes parades as King Edward, while Cara was often sold as King Edward, which was a real challenge during the 1980s. The variety came through that sticky period and I think its future is now very much assured. UK acreage remains static, and it is the only potato variety that has some degree of public recognition. Today it is still in the Top 20 of varieties grown in the UK, with its striking red-splashed, cream-skinned oval tubers. It is still a benchmark for quality, and if you are growing King Edward in your garden you have my total respect.

LADY BALFOUR

Named after the founder of the Soil Association, Lady Eve Balfour, this variety is aimed at the growing and financially significant organic market. Here the need is for excellent blight resistance to achieve a marketable yield, and this variety is a decent attempt. It produces very high yields on land low in fertility, which is interesting and expands the potential. Agronomic attributes include reasonable blight resistance and partial PCN resistance to both strains. Tubers are mixed in size and the stolons tend to remain attached to the plant, which means that mechanically harvested tubers bruise easily. A white-skinned oval-shaped variety, for me it may not carry enough merit in terms of taste, storability and final appearance.

LADY CLAIRE

Lady Claire is a crisping variety with excellent fry colour, particularly after long storage. Its aim is to bolster quality for crispers at the end of the storage season in May and June, thereby offering a year-round supply to the crisp industry. The thin, yellow-skinned, light-yellow-fleshed tubers are round to oval in shape, and produce a very good yield and dry matter content. Lady Claire has a high resistance to damage and bruising, and early maturity could be a key attribute. It has good resistance to one strain of PCN.

LADY ROSETTA

Holland • 1988 • second early

This is a very successful crisping variety, with high dry matters of around 22 to 24% and low reducing sugars. It has rapid growth and early final crop maturity and can be processed direct from the field or after long-term storage. It is an excellent potato and the most popular early season and short-term storage crisping variety. The tubers are medium-sized, with a rough netted red skin and round shape and shallow eyes. Lady Rosetta is also suitable for starch and mashed potatoes.

The variety is high-yielding and has high tuber numbers. The size distribution is uniform and development of the crop rapid. Lady Rosetta will produce excellent results in a range of conditions, with good drought tolerance and response to irrigation, rapid leaf development and good ground cover. It is very good until Christmas, then more challenging due to outgrades.

It is a very popular variety that may have just peaked with so many new offerings coming on to the market. It has very good all-round disease resistance including to one strain of PCN. Low blight resistance is a negative, but this obviously has not affected its success.

C. J. Meijer is a well-established Dutch breeding company with a strong pedigree of success. The varieties are prefixed 'Lady' (though not Lady Balfour), and others include such as Accord, Bionica, Fambo, Melody and Orchestra.

LUMPER

This famous historical variety was caught up in the middle of the tragic famine in Ireland. It was the dominant variety at the time, well ahead in acreage of the varieties Cup and Rocks. Ironically, Lumper is no more susceptible to blight than King Edward. However, the overall quality of the retained Lumper seed being planted at the time of the famine, aligned to the flat-bed system of production, made the variety very prone to several kinds of infection. All potato varieties in Ireland, England and Europe collapsed during this period – the Lumper was not alone.

The culinary performance is poor, and it was rated in its day as being suitable for animal feed. The texture is wet and soapy with little if any taste. 'A poor man's potato' went the marketing spin. However, Lumper did crop well. The white-skinned circular and knotted tubers do catch the eye, but after a few days of trying to peel them the modern smoother introductions have their value.

The Irish Potato Famine of 1845-50 contributed to the deaths of two million people. It remains a key political and agronomic milestone and well worth understanding (see Cecil Woodham-Smith, *The Great Hunger*, and Canon John O'Rourke, *The Great Irish Famine* – both are classics).

The Irish famine shaped the future of potato-breeding with many new varieties imported from the USA. Potato blight today is still a great challenge as it continually changes its composition.

MAGNUM BONUM

England • 1876 • maincrop

Bred by James Clark, the seedling was selected by the famous Victorian horticulturalist Shirley Hibberd from a Paterson's Victoria and Early Rose cross. Magnum Bonum became the Victorian variety of choice for farmers and gardeners alike. Its launch year of 1876 was challenging, with many reports of rotten tubers and poor yields: Magnum Bonum produces 'all tops and no bottoms' was the tone of the reports. However, Clark defended the potato in the press and it soon gained ground.

The Sutton's Seeds catalogue of 1877 takes up the marketing:

'A splendid new late kidney, which has hitherto been almost free from disease. The tubers are large, of excellent shape and cook well before they are fully mature. It is the heaviest cropping English potato we have ever seen, and the flavour most excellent. The erect habit of growth and colour of the flower are perfectly distinct from all other kidneys.'

It was simply the best in its day for yield and widely respected for its culinary quality, and peaked as England's most widely grown potato, its popularity having been built on eye-witness accounts of fantastic yields and great tasting experience … and marketing.

It has white skin and flesh with a smooth kidney shape, a good yield, but on the late side. The tubers are prone to rapid greening, so ensure protection from light at storage time. Magnum Bonum was used in the parentage of King Edward, and it is a shame that it is not offered by today's seed companies; its historic significance is worthy of attention alone.

MAJESTIC

Scotland • 1911 • maincrop

Archibald Findlay from Fife, Scotland, bred the Majestic potato. It was the most successful introduction of the 20th century and cemented Findlay's position in potato-breeding history. He had two farms, one in his homeland and the other temporarily in Lincolnshire, the centre of English potato-growing.

Majestic success was twofold. First, it was a reliable chipper for the UK. We must have our fish and chips, and for 60 years through two World Wars Majestic met that need. Second, it was almost entirely grown in the great rich, fertile soils of Lincolnshire. While other regions experimented with Doon Star, Gladstone, Arran Banner, etc, Lincolnshire planted and planted Majestic. As late as 1959 the variety still accounted for 59% of all maincrops in England.

However, the tubers were not of high quality, turning grey on cooking. They made a kind of lumpy mash and were easily outperformed by King Edward. So did the culinary limitations of Majestic make King Edward look good? Whatever your view, you have to credit the sheer size of acreage gained and its longevity. Majestic's fall came when Maris Piper became available.

The Majestic plants can appear spindly and a tone of green closer to matted lime. The leaves are very close-set with clear points, and the flowers are numerous. The tubers are large and are slow to sprout; consequently good-quality Majestics store well through the winter.

Archibald Findlay (1841-1921) was a local (Fife) hero, a pioneering and controversial potato breeder. Many of his varieties were accused of being re-marketed from former selections. Findlay will forever be associated with the potato boom, claims about blight resistance, and for breeding the most successful UK variety of the 20th century.

MARFONA
Holland • 1975 • second early

Huge quantities of this variety are grown around the world. Marfona has built its success on the ability to throw very high yields with a large baker-sized percentage. It has a much loved creamy-yellow colour and texture, and the taste is pleasant, often described as buttery.

Marfona has a round to oval shape with a smooth to medium-smooth skin and pale yellow flesh. The eyes are shallow, but have an increasing tendency to deepen when the plant receives too much nitrogen. This also has an influence on outgrades, which can be annoyingly high. Agronomy is fair with good dormancy, but poor blight and no PCN resistance has not hampered Marfona's progress; common scab resistance is also poor. To cap it all, the slugs like Marfona too.

Marfona now dominates the second early plantings in the UK. If you disregard Maris Peer (new potatoes) and Lady Rosetta (crisping), Marfona is only behind Estima and Maris Piper in UK planted acreage. It is perhaps now oversold, as it is best eaten before Christmas, after which it becomes wet. If you eat out in pubs and order a baked potato, the chances are that you will be served Marfona.

MARIS BARD
England • 1972 • first early

This was an excellent variety in its day with its early harvest of bright, white good-sized tubers. It has a good yield and a pleasant taste, and became the true early variety for most of England, with only Pembroke and Cornwall reluctant to take it on. It is susceptible to blackleg and a bit of a slug-catcher in most gardens, but the tubers boil well and retain their shape when cooked. It can be eaten as a new potato as well as roasted or baked. Commercial samples have too many outgrades, which rather held this one back when compared to Maris Peer.

MARIS PEER

Originally bred for the canning market, Maris Peer has become the first choice of most supermarket buyers for the washed, small new potato trade. It gives lots of small round tubers, which stay within the medium-size bracket required by supermarkets. This really makes it a great potato to use for all parties. It is not a variety for large tubers, and the dry matter remains low, so the texture is firm, whether harvested young or mature. The cooked tubers hold their bright white colour and shape, but taste is compromised for functionality, which is true of many post-war varieties. Maris Peer produces close-leaved and compact plants with an abundance of nice purple flowers. The agronomy is now dated with poor blight resistance, susceptibility to PCN, drought and, to top it all, slugs; in fact, anything prefixed 'Maris' is pretty tasty for slugs. Yet Maris Peer handles well in commercial harvesting and storing. In short, it is a good commercial potato.

Despite its second early classification, Maris Peer is the UK's most commonly grown new potato, and some 45 years after its introduction it commands a massive acreage in the UK, making it the third most popular potato grown in 2009. It is also grown in Majorca, Spain, Israel, Italy and a dozen other leading potato countries.

The Plant Breeding Institute (PBI) was established in 1912 at the instigation of the then Board of Agriculture. In 1987 it was sold to a private company. Today, the site at Cambridge is the home of a very smart Waitrose supermarket branch with the address Maris Lane, Cambridge.

MARIS PIPER

A worthy champion of a variety, this was the most popular potato grown in the UK in 2009, and has been for some time; it is a favourite of chippers, consumers and farmers. Lots of potatoes make good chips, but this makes great chips – it is as simple as that. The tubers are oval, sometimes extended, and shallow-eyed on a cream skin with white flesh. There is no sign of after-cooking discoloration, but some disintegration on boiling can be expected. Maris Piper also bakes and roasts to a high standard.

Maris Piper saved potato-growing in many eastern counties due to its resistance to one strain of potato cyst nematode. The significance of a variety that resisted the main strain of PCN (G. *rostochiensis*) in the early 1960s was huge, as crop losses were questioning the very viability of potato-growing. Maris Piper replaced Pentland Crown, Pentland Hawk and Majestic in Lincolnshire and Cambridgeshire.

It is, however, useless for growing in the garden; the slugs and scab love it, blight resistance is poor and you will probably be disappointed with the yields if the plant becomes dry. Yet for farmers and those on the silts of Lincolnshire, it is probably the best potato in the world. It is the No 1 potato planted in the UK and, provided its integrity is not compromised, will be for some time.

The Plant Breeding Institute/Plant Breeding International site in Maris Lane, Cambridge, achieved a degree of immortality by launching the varieties prefixed 'Maris'. However, there were many others such as Cromwell, Drayton, Foxton, Kingston, Lindsay, Picador, Pilgrim, Rocket, Saxon, Sierra, Sovereign, etc. The story continues with Cygnet Potatoes Ltd.

MAYAN GOLD

The was the first marketed *Solanum phureja* cross from the Scottish Crop Research Institute (SCRI). It produces small, elongated tubers with a yellow skin, deep yellow flesh and a distinctive almond flavour when baked. The dry matter is very high, so it is not suitable for boiling. Considerable interest has been shown by UK supermarkets, respecting the massive work to bring a new species of potato to the market. Mayan Gold has good resistance to common scab, but poor PCN resistance. It is marketed strongly on its delicate culinary platform, which has to be welcome. The S. *phureja* species has little or no dormancy and, although much work has been done by the breeders, the *phureja* types of Mayan Gold, Twilight and Queen all remain very short in dormancy.

> ***Solanum phureja*** is a species of *Solanum*. It is renowned for wild coloured flesh, a great buttery texture and no dormancy. The tubers sprout within days of harvest. The species potential as a niche variety was recognised by Prof George Mackay of the Scottish Crop Research Institute, who pioneered this work. The 'Mayan' series is the prefix name for the development of the species into varieties with longer dormancy.

MAY QUEEN

England • 1900 • first early

May Queen is an old-fashioned kidney shape with bright white, smooth skins becoming netted close to maturity. Some coloration may be seen in mature tubers. It is a really nice eating potato with a close texture becoming floury with maturity. This is what the Sutton's Seeds catalogue of 1933 had to say about May Queen:

'Every season we sell a very large tonnage of this variety. Suttons May Queen is unrivalled for framework and it also yields a very early crop in the open ground. The kidney-shaped tubers attain a good size quickly and excellent specimens for the table may be dug while the haulm is still green. The fact that large acreages are every year planted for marketing, especially in the early potato districts of Cornwall, testifies to its outstanding qualities.'

By the outbreak of the Second World War, the variety was in steep decline. It is very blight-prone and needs careful handling. This is another example of a gardener's potato not really mixing well with the ever-increasingly mechanised handling of the commercial world.

MEINS EARLY ROUND

Scotland • 1916 • second early

This colourful, round, old-fashioned potato is ideal for the show bench. It has dramatic stripy red markings at the rose end and the crop yield is satisfactory, with tubers of medium but variable size It has quite a mealy texture, having a high dry matter, and is best used as a baker if you can get good tuber size. It is prone to most agronomic issues. Only a small commercial acreage was achieved, and by the outbreak of the Second World War it was only to be found growing in gardens. I have grown this one for many years, mainly as the coloration is so dramatic and the small baked tubers are mealy and tasty.

MOZART

Holland • 2006 • maincrop

Is this the Romano or Desiree replacement? Mozart (in the centre of the painting, with Melody [see page 143] on the left and Marfona [see page 86] on the right) has lots going for it, with high, even yields of red-skinned tubers and a creamy yellow flesh. The shape can be oval to a quite protruded oval. For me, the taste is better than Romano but not as full or developed as Desiree. However, the agronomy is an improvement on both, with good blight resistance and resistance to one strain of PCN.

Mozart is a slow starter (and I mean slow) and maturity is on the late side of maincrop. Chitting is recommended. Mozart has a moderate dry matter and is therefore functional for all requirements without excelling. The tuber size is less than Romano, but the shape is much more consistent than Desiree, so there are fewer outgrades. Plenty of tubers form, which makes the final yield very good. Introduced to Waitrose by Dr Simon Bowen, it is still early days for the variety but it appears very useful, though not a threat to the high quality of Desiree.

MR BRESEE

USA • 1870 • second early

This one came over from the USA after the famine debacle, when UK breeders were for many years trialing new sorts to fill the gaps left by the arrival of potato blight. The tubers are a flat, kidney shape progressing to a kind of squashed banana shape when large. The pretty pink skin contains a bright white flesh that can be strongly coloured pink around the vascular ring, but this is not consistent. It keeps this red pigmentation when cooked and makes a devilish mashed potato. It has a very nice taste on the sandy soils here in Fleet, but is soapy on heavier soils. The yields were outstanding in the one season I grew it. The plants are very spreading, large-leafed and a lighter shade of green but very virus prone.

It was bred by Albert Bresee from Vermont, USA, a hobby breeder whose varieties made a significant contribution to potato-growing in the UK. His introductions included Early Rose, Bresee's Prolific and Bresee's Peerless. During the Victorian period American-bred varieties were openly traded and highly praised for their good blight resistance.

> **Albert Bresee** was an American independent potato variety breeder. His significant contribution was the use he made of seedlings selected from stock supplied by Rev C. E. Goodrich of Utica. From this the variety Early Rose was introduced and several others, such as Prolific and Peerless, which were exported to Europe. Early Rose went on to be the parent of Russet Burbank, Magnum Bonum and many more.

NADINE

Scotland • 1987 • second early

Nadine is another commercial winner from Jack Dunnett and Caithness Potatoes. It has succeeded in most countries where it has been marketed, especially Australia, where it has performed outstandingly – yields of 100 tonnes per hectare have been achieved under ideal conditions, which is remarkable! A yield of 60-70 tonnes per hectare would be very good in UK. Nadine is certainly a variety that responds well to modern farming, and is currently in the Top 20 of all varieties grown in the UK, but the acreage may have peaked.

It produces high yields of uniform attractive tubers, so is ideal for the washed, pre-packed supermarket trade. The skins are bright and egg-like smooth, and the variety has good agronomy, including excellent scab and bruising resistance together with dual resistance and tolerance to both strains of PCN. Nadine has a low dry matter, which renders it unsuitable for baking, chipping or roasting. I find the taste bland and on many soils the texture is wet to the point of being insipid. However, the firm texture remains good for boiling and steaming. It is a very good choice for the local horticultural show. Use before Christmas.

NAVAN

Northern Ireland • 1987 • maincrop

Navan was bred as a Maris Piper replacement. It possesses good, all-round cooking qualities and is also suitable for the chip market. The tubers are oval in shape with shallow eyes, creamy skins and flesh. Agronomy is good, with notable resistance to one strain of PCN and tolerance to the other. Navan has a dry matter slightly higher than Maris Piper, and the tubers can be quite large. A worthy attempt, Navan is now grown abroad, but it is now more than 20 years since it was released and I think we have seen all that it is going to do. It is a good variety that should have done better.

NICOLA

Germany • 1973 • early maincrop

In the 1970s the most influential man in the potato trade was the general manager of the Cyprus Potato Marketing Board, Andreas Saviddes. Cyprus was a key exporter of delicious potatoes to the UK in the spring and early summer, and this variety was therefore aimed at Cyprus, due to its similarity to an existing variety, Spunta. It proved to be much better than Spunta in shape, taste and yield, and Andreas Saviddes effectively launched it and ensured its success.

The plants are very even with dark-green foliage and white flowers. Nicola produces an abundance of elongated yellow-skinned, yellow-fleshed tubers. Usually they are clean-skinned and free from pest damage. The texture is waxy and the yellow flesh eats with the fresh sweetness of the Mediterranean. If left to go cold there is little, if any, dulling of the tuber and the sweet taste is retained, so it is ideal for a potato salad. The larger tubers bake well and also makes good chips. Nicola potatoes sold in supermarkets are often small-sized and described as a new potato. To get the best from Nicola grow it almost to the point when the haulms have fallen and turned a light yellow; this will ensure that the tubers are large and fully developed. If you like Wilja, try this one as an improved culinary version.

Nicola is susceptible to blight but resistant to one strain of PCN. The tubers, when stressed, can show a faint pink colouration. Ridge up well as the elongated tubers will become exposed to the light and many good potatoes ruined.

ORLA

This flexible variety is aimed at the commercial pre-packing sector. Very grower friendly, it produces high yields with reasonable baker content if planted with a full term intended. The oval, shallow-eyed, white, thin-skinned tubers have a light-yellow flesh and the skin quality is usually free from disease. However, the tubers are quick to show greening, and the dry matter is low, which in this case leads to a soft-textured potato. The flavour does not shine, but it is functional. It can be harvested as new, or left to bulk and sold later in the season.

Orla is a worthy choice for organic production. In Ireland it has made good progress, gaining acreage from Estima and Marfona. Against Estima it outperforms on tuber blight, foliage blight, powdery scab and blackleg, and regularly produces more stems than Marfona or Estima.

OSPREY

A Sante/Stroma crossed with Kestrel, Osprey (on the left in the painting, with Picasso – see page 148) is said to be the improved Kestrel. An offering from Jack Dunnett, it has much of the same agronomy and a greater yield than Kestrel, which is quite important and the main driver in its success. Osprey shows improved tuber numbers on most but not all soils, and the tubers make good size, well above the minimum of 45mm, so there are few outgrades. Osprey has better blight resistance than Kestrel, which may be why it does well in Scotland. The overall PCN resistance/tolerance is good to both strains, so in agronomic terms it is indeed an improved Kestrel.

However, the texture and taste is, in my humble opinion, mediocre. It performs its duties in the kitchen without excelling in any area – it boils, roasts, chips and bakes, but food excellence it is not.

Its part-red tubers are large and thin-skinned; the shape is a good oval, sometimes round and sometimes quite dumpy-looking. The tuber's appearance is a creamy-white flesh and the red sometimes has faint dots around the eyes, rather than splashes.

Currently Osprey has five times the acreage of Kestrel, and in 2008 ranked 19th in the UK plantings table; it is also to be seen in many other countries. It is exclusive to a large Scottish-based supermarket supplier, and is proving to be a very popular variety indeed.

> Dr Simon Bowen writes, 'Charlotte is my favourite potato. It is a variety that has developed almost in parallel with my career in potatoes and as such it has presented a range of agronomic challenges for me to work on over this period. As a salad variety it was a ground-breaker, delivering a unique point of difference in taste and texture. The larger tubers develop a light floury texture and bake and roast deliciously. If you have not baked a large Charlotte I recommend that you do.'

PENTLAND CROWN

Scotland • 1959 • early maincrop

The tubers are large round to oval, with white skin and bright white flesh. The agronomy is poor by today's expectations with the variety is prone to blight, hollow heart and slug attack, having no PCN resistance. However, it does have very good common scab resistance. The tubers grow wide in the ridge, with the long stolons often pushing the large tubers outside the soil-covered ridge, which makes greening a challenge. Growers turned to Pentland Crown as Majestic tired, and in the 1960s it came second only to Majestic for table potatoes, so one needs to see this variety's success in that context.

On poorer soils, where Maris Piper was not suitable, growers in Somerset and Herefordshire mainly found themselves growing Pentland Crown. It was high-yielding and often grown on virgin land, where it produced very large crops and acreage dramatically rose. Initial quality reports rated it as a satisfactory potato, but as the variety grew to almost saturated levels consumer attention was drawn to ever-increasing amounts of after-cooking blackening, possibly exacerbated by fertiliser use. Whatever the cause, it helped Pentland Crown on to the emerging supermarkets' blacklist.

In the early 1970s Sainsbury's placed a full-colour advert in the national press stating that the variety was so bad it would not stock it. It was the first occasion when a leading supermarket had so publicly questioned what growers were doing.

PENTLAND DELL

Scotland • 1961 • early maincrop

These long white-skinned tubers almost beg to be made into chips, and that was its role, with thousands of acres destined for crisps and frozen chips. Pentland Dell accounted for 11% of all potato acreage in 1968. The foliage is a bit spindly and easily broken, a setback from which this variety does not recover well. This in turn encourages the formation of very small potatoes, which never reach a decent size. To avoid this for home use, a well-chitted potato is required, and planted into warm soil. it is a very high-yielding variety, with reasonable agronomy but no PCN resistance.

The breeder of Pentland Dell was a young Jack Dunnett, based at the Pentlandfield breeding station near Edinburgh. It has now generally been replaced by higher-yielding alternatives. This and all the varieties prefixed 'Pentland' were named after the hills to the north of the breeding station.

PINK FIR APPLE

England • before 1850 • maincrop

This is a fun variety with very long finger-like knobbly tubers that taste like a new potato all year round – this was the Victorian's Christmas trick, to bring out Pink Fir Apple in mid-winter as a potato with a new potato texture. The cooked colour is a dark grey/yellow, especially after a short time in cold storage. This very vigorous plant yields a high number of stems with dozens of often small tubers forming very close under the roots. Harvesting is a bit of a job as the plant accrues lots of secondary roots. Pink Fir Apple is a blight-catcher and has few if any redeeming agronomic features. Space wide and double-ridge to stop the long tubers from protruding.

Although it has had a relatively tiny commercial acreage all its life, Pink Fir Apple has a loyal following. It is one of our oldest varieties and should have a medal for surviving while quietly never gaining any more than token acreage.

The painting above is typical. From high-grade seed, the progeny should be more uniform in length, but this is not always the case.

In his 1836 manual Lawson describes, with suspicious similarity, a variety called 'Rose Finn Apple', a name that is also attributed to Pink Fir Apple in parts of the USA. The only significance of this is that it makes Pink Fir Apple a very old variety indeed and suggests that the variety may be even older than the date I have attributed to it.

98

RATTE

France • 1872 • early maincrop

This variety has a few other names, such as Asparges and Kipfler. If you are looking for a true salad potato, look no further. Ratte is long, like pink Fir Apple, but without the knobbly bits and a smoother creamy-yellow skin. The texture is waxy, firm and tastes like a buttery chestnut. Hot or cold, summer or winter, Ratte is the benchmark in salad culinary performance. I like mine cold with the skin on and maybe dipped in olive oil.

Seed quality has been an issue, which has given the impression that this is a low-yielding variety, but from clean seed yields are very high. I prefer my Ratte tubers as large as possible. Plant spaciously and try to limit water at tuber initiation. Once this period has passed, watering is returned to normal with a foliar feed, and the stock harvested is much larger. The variety has useless agronomy with no blight, PCN or drought resistance, so ensure that good seed is purchased.

Descriptions of varieties very much like Ratte appear in Lawson's manual of 1836, and carry the name Asparagus potato.

RECORD

Holland • 1932 • early maincrop

Many of the potatoes described in this book are aimed at processing, which means that they have high dry matter. Record held this ground for many years, being the first choice for crisp-makers, remaining the mainstay of processing production until the 1960s, when a slow decline set in. It is still grown today, but on a much reduced scale.

It gives heavy crops of round, medium-sized tubers that fit the machines perfectly. The skin is rough and golden brown in colour, and the eyes are shallow. Its agronomy is dated now, but it was a landmark variety in its day.

RED DUKE OF YORK

Holland • 1942 • first early

This variety boasts a truly excellent, stunning dark red/crimson colour, of almost alarming intensity – people always comment. It is another sport found from a Duke of York crop and proves to be identical. It is very early to crop and if eaten young gives the same delicious Duke of York taste. It bulks quickly and by mid-summer you can expect large tubers that can be baked. It has the potential to be the first set skinned red on the market, and is one of my favourites in the field or garden. The foliage is strong with leaves and stems red pigmented, and the final sample can be heavily netted, so Red Duke of York is best on a strong-bodied loam. The tubers soon develop high dry matter, so when mature they are best baked or roasted, and people seem to love the nutty taste. It will collapse when boiled in a saucepan, so steaming is an option.

This is one of the few varieties to which you could become addicted. I plant it in late February and start eating it in early June. As the crop matures, follow the change in tuber texture from waxy to floury. Harvest the lot and store. Job done! Facing the winter with a shed full of Red Duke of Yorks may make you face nature's short days and long nights with a bit more optimism. Despite being identical to Duke of York, I think this sport is stronger, but take no chances. The early harvest will help miss the ravages of blight, but in a wet season blight protection will be required. Ensure that you harvest on a good day and store the tubers when dry.

Red Duke of York is a good example of why I write about potato varieties. By making people aware of the culinary diversity at our fingertips, we can continue to support varieties that suit all tastes. From no seed acreage in 1990, Red Duke of York has around 10 hectares of seed grown in the UK. In recent years this variety has been sold in supermarkets such as Waitrose. It has also been made into crisps and of course as seed for gardeners. It is great that this variety is now grown, but the acreage is very small.

RED KING EDWARD

Scotland • 1916 • maincrop

This variety is identical to King Edward, and is a red-skinned variant found in a King Edward crop. But it is not the only variant: a purple-splashed King Edward exists, and Yetholm Gypsy is another. They achieve special variety status due to their popularity and, in particular, their stableness. So from Red King Edward you can expect tubers that are 95% all red with odd flecks of white in small areas. The culinary quality is identical and just as delicious.

Red King Edward was one of the most popular variants listed as a single variety. From soon after its release until the 1960s its acreage was always in the Top 10 maincrop varieties for UK plantings. However, as acreage of King Edward declined, so did this, and by the late 1990s was on the edge of extinction. Waitrose initiated virus-tested stem cuttings and micro-propagation to bring it back from cold storage and seed was patiently multiplied. It is very much a Christmas potato and, as far as I know, the only potato variety to be included in a supermarket's Christmas TV advertising.

The agronomy is identical to King Edward, but the plant and final tubers have subtle differences. The plant is very vigorous and often produces faint purple and white flowers. The tubers have a stronger red coloration density than King Edward and the yields more consistent than its parent. Like King Edward, attention should be paid to the tendency to throw high numbers of tubers.

Despite a variety having the same DNA, one should expect differing manifestations of behaviour. It is this fact that makes sports or variants of varieties interesting to us all. So keep a look out when you harvest any variety.

REMARKA
Holland • 1992 • early maincrop

This vigorous-growing variety is suitable for organic growing. It has high tuber blight resistance, moderate foliage blight resistance, and is resistant to one strain of PCN, but there is a tendency for hollow heart. The tuber count is low, but large, and reaches a marketable yield quickly given the variety's maincrop classification. The tubers are yellow-fleshed and round to oval, and the cooking qualities are highly rated, especially as a baker with the even dry matter allowing good all-round culinary performance. This is a good choice for early baker (large tuber) content, and has very good dormancy.

ROCKET
England • 1987 • first early

This British variety comes from the company that bred Maris Piper and, as the name suggests, it is a very early potato. That is its main point really – the sheer speed of growth. At harvest, the young tubers are fine, but later in the season they are prone to cracking; taste can also disappoint. As they race on for full growth, further skin and tuber problems seem to occur. Still, if you want the earliest crops, this is the one to grow. The tubers are white-skinned and round with medium-depth eyes. The agronomy is good, but acreage is now in decline.

ROMANO

Holland • 1978 • early maincrop

Very good yields of perfectly round, smooth, red-skinned and white-fleshed tubers can be expected, with deep eyes. It is early for a maincrop, and on light soils in the south I would treat it more of a second early. The Romano plants have large leaves, which are vigorous and spreading. It is very good in resisting slugs, and for many gardeners this will be a key attribute. There is no PCN resistance, but that should not be a worry for those with good soils on long rotations. The blight resistance, while better than Desiree, is still modest. If grown successfully the yields can be very high.

Organic growers have dabbled with Romano with limited success. The trick is to get it growing quickly and with a marketable yield under the plant before August. Harvesting should be completed on most soils by the middle of the same month, but the cooked tubers from heavier land can show some discoloration when boiled. Romano has picked up some bad press, which may be down to the very high rates of nitrogen placed on some crops. Romano was aimed to be the Desiree replacement, and when first released these cooking discrepancies did not show themselves. While it scores many points over Desiree, taste is not one of them. Romano is simply different, being more breakable in texture. For all cooking purposes it is fine, and especially suitable for late-season use as it stores well and has a good dormancy period. It can be used into April, and commercial growers keep this one until July.

Romano gained thousands of acres in the UK and became a widely grown variety, but today is in decline.

ROOSTER

Ireland • 1993 • early maincrop

This is the most common variety now consumed in Ireland and a real winner of a variety. To dislodge Kerr's Pink from the No 1 spot has to take some doing, and it is Rooster that takes the credit.

This dark-red-skinned potato has high dry matter and bright white flesh, and is an excellent all-round potato if you like a texture on the dry side. It produces excellent French fries and is also perfect for mashing and roasting, although it will fall apart in the pan when boiled. There is no PCN resistance but reasonable blight resistance. It was aimed at the processing sector, but has developed a wider appeal.

The real story behind Rooster comes in the marketing. Albert Bartlett Ltd has sole rights in the UK and has invested a significant sum of money in a range of media activity. By keeping it branded it has forced a place onto supermarket shelves, which makes it unique as the first branded potato variety. It is also the first potato variety to be marketed professionally with all kinds of market penetration measures. Somewhere in this there is a lesson.

It has won several awards such as the Scottish Food & Drink Excellence Award, and also gained the title of 'Best Fruit or Vegetable Product 2005' and 'Best Healthy Eating Marketing Campaign 2005'.

So how good is Rooster? It has high dry matter, is mealy and has a middle-of-the-road taste. If you like British Queen or Kerr's Pink, Rooster is a natural progression. I tend to like a softer potato, so Rooster is not on my list. When it comes to the red-skinned varieties, the closest comparison to Rooster in texture is Red Duke of York. Rooster was the 17th most commonly grown variety in the UK in 2008, and I expect this will improve further in the years to come, unless of course the marketing stops.

ROSEVAL

France • 1950 • second early

One of my favourites, this is a superb French salad potato. When cooked, Roseval has a close, very waxy texture, and when cold it retains its colour and shape. In all recipes where the potato must stay together, Roseval is great; it is my first choice when making a potato salad, as is easier to use than Ratte in both size and shape.

This deep-red, shallow-eyed, pear-shaped potato can sometimes be a bit misshapen if the tubers are allowed to grow too large – control this by tighter spacing at planting. Roseval needs fresh soil and is sensitive to short rotations. The plant is tall spreading and the leaves heavily pigmented; this red pigmentation is sometimes also seen in the tubers and can be heavy. It is susceptible to pest and diseases, so that is a drawback, but the yields may just surprise you, at 70-plus tubers if the plant is allowed to go full term. I think that is well worth the wait.

It is best harvested when the haulms (plants) are nearly mature, i.e. showing light yellowing in the leaves. Roseval has a number of rivals, namely Franceline and Rosa, which while worthy varieties do not have the same strong taste.

ROYAL KIDNEY

Scotland • 1899 • second early

From Archibald Findlay came this rival to the hugely successful International Kidney. This one did not do that badly either, being grown around the world and for many years the mainstay of the Majorcan export trade to the UK.

The tubers are small, which is perfect for a new potato, while the shape is a true kidney with a smooth cream to yellow skin. Under stress the tubers can show coloration around the eyes. Royal Kidney has a delicious taste, and the development of dry matter is in the medium range, so there is some flexibility on harvesting dates. The yield is reasonable with the tubers of medium size and very suitable for use as a new potato. The off-white tubers retain their shape fully.

As you would expect, Royal Kidney's agronomy is now very dated. It is prone to blight and of course has no PCN resistance. My preference I think goes with the history, as Royal Kidney, worthy as it is of greater attention, stands second in my taste rating to International Kidney.

RUSSET BURBANK

USA • 1875 • early maincrop

This is one of many brown, russet-skinned potato varieties in the US, but is probably the most famous. It was bred and brought to the market by Luther Burbank, an independent potato-breeder and horticulturist.

Its presence in the UK is entirely down to McDonald's wanting it as their first-choice variety for making chips. Russet Burbank is a long potato that is ideal for chips. It has a tough russet skin, and the bright white flesh retains its colour; with perfect dry matter, the chips are golden when cooked in thin strips. It is very different from Maris Piper.

Rather than celebrate the heritage of such a lovely variety, Russet Burbank became caught up in the genetically modified debate, as in the US a genetically modified herbicide-resistant Russet Burbank was developed.

Russet Burbank is prone to blight and PCN; however, the plants are vigorous and spreading, the strong stems thick and angled. Tubers can be large, long and cylindrical, or slightly flattened with a russet skin. This variety is good for all cooking purposes, not just chips. There are many Russet varieties in the US, which should not be confused with this one, which is still widely grown in the US and highly rated.

> **Luther Burbank** (1849-1926) was a brilliant American botanist who introduced more than 800 varieties of flowers and more specifically peaches, nectarines and the famous Santa Rosa plum. I do not know how he found time to create the Russet Burbank potato, but we can be thankful that he did.

SANTE

This is one of the first modern introductions to have dual PCN resistance/tolerance, and the importance of this for those commercial growers infested by PCN cannot be overstated. This is also relevant to gardeners, where potato land has been over-cropped.

Sante has been widely grown and is still worthy of consideration even if it is now a bit outdated. The tubers have a flat round shape, with moderately deep eyes; the skin is white and the flesh matches. Sante is a useful functional potato in the kitchen; it is fine as a boiled potato, but when all is considered it is a bland variety. Roasting, baking and chipping are not Sante's specialities.

The agronomy of the variety is very good, making it suitable for organic growers. There is also reasonable blight resistance, although not as good as the Sharpo range. Virus resistance, handling and other skin defects also show good resistance, and the final yield is high.

> **Agrico** is a multinational potato breeding and marketing company based in Holland. It is involved with a large range of varieties including Ditta, Fianna, Fontane, Markies, Picasso, Premiere, Romano, Sante, Wilja and many more.

SARPO MIRA

Its outstanding blight resistance, including great recovery from blight attack, makes this a landmark variety surpassing all others I have seen, and boasts the best blight resistance of the Sarpo range. The growth is slow to start, then spreading with a wide stem spacing and airy habit.

The dormancy is very long and the variety stores well. The downside is taste, which is very bland and part mealy. It has no other outstanding agronomic attributes, but I find that it performs the best in drought conditions.

SAXON

I spotted this one when the tubers were numbered from a breeding plot in Maris Lane in Cambridge. It was one of the last introductions from the Plant Breeding Institute, the home of Maris Piper. My reason for choosing Saxon for Waitrose was the combination of taste, shape and yield; having been so critical of the lack of taste in modern potato-breeding, it was great to find a British new variety that I actually wanted to eat.

Initial crops ran into all sorts of emergence issues, from which the marketing company and the growers have now learned. Do not plant Saxon in cool conditions and ideally chit the seed. Plant tubers with their eyes open into a warm soil. It has excellent blackleg and virus resistance, as well as resistance to one type of PCN; blight resistance is modest. The plant growth is strong and early, with a very high baker (large tuber) percentage; the tubers are oval, with white skin and bright white flesh. Saxon boils, bakes, roasts and chips with good texture and freedom from cooking blackening or disintegration.

Saxon is now seventh in UK potato plantings and is also making an appearance on the worldwide stage. I have therefore watched this one grow with interest and a wry smile.

SHARPES EXPRESS

England • 1901 • first early

There are dozens of books and records that place this one up there with Duke of York as a fine-quality potato, but it is very different. It throws medium-sized tubers with bright white skin and flesh, and, like Duke of York, the dry matter rapidly develops to make this a mealy variety, so ensure that it is dug soon after flowering for best flavour. However, it is not a modern potato and its final product may not always have the consistency demanded.

Sharpes Express prefers land with some body in it. It tends to be a bit late for a first early, more of a Pentland Javelin in timing. It must be well watered at the early stages, and is susceptible to nearly everything, so I think it is one for the early season only.

The tubers are pear-shaped, tapering at the heel end, and the skin colour is white to cream, with shallow eyes. It can make quite large tubers with yields variable from plant to plant.

Sharpes Express is one of three varieties from Charles Sharpe of Sleaford included in this book. Never widely grown, it kept a modest acreage until 1950, mostly in Cornwall, since when it has been used almost solely for the garden trade. The crop timing and final yield hastened its decline. Sharpes Express had less than 10 hectares of seed grown in Scotland in 2010.

SHETLAND BLACK

Scotland • before 1836 • maincrop

This is an excellent, if rough, black-skinned potato, whose creamy flesh is often laced with a purple ring near the surface. It is a superb-tasting potato, if a little shy on yield, and is best baked, due to the very high dry matter. Tuber size is generally small to medium, and the shape is a long oval, sometimes a bit like a pear. It has poor agronomy, so expect all kinds of trouble and ensure really good seed.

Shetland Black is one of the old potato varieties that has made a bit of a comeback – it was really too

good to be locked in a museum. I am pleased to say Waitrose has sold small quantities for the past ten years, and that seed can be obtained through specialist seed suppliers. Shetland Black was never a widely grown variety, and probably never will be, but it is a must for the potato enthusiast.

Also known as Black Kidney, 'Shetland Blacks' are described in Lawson's Manual of 1836 and the tuber description is very similar, hence the revised date of its introduction.

SKERRY BLUE

Ireland • 1800 • late maincrop

This very old Irish variety is blue-skinned, but cream-fleshed. It was highly praised for its blight-resisting capacity during the famine, which it still has! it is not as high yielding as Lumper, to which it was always second. It was once grown in England as far

north as Westmorland, and also Wales. An important variety in Ireland, it gained around 4% of the acreage. Very rare and tasty, it is one of the oldest varieties still around, but its lack of immunity to wart diseases encouraged the rise of Arran Victory.

SUNRISE

Sunrise produces a very high yield of part-red tubers, which can be really large. The variety shows good drought resistance, which is proving very useful in hot climates, as well as resistance to common scab. Its reaction to PCN is less clear, but it does have some tolerance. It is a Valor x Cultra cross, both of which excel in functionality as opposed to taste. Sunrise itself has high dry matter, so expect a more mealy texture

It is bred by entry from Zella Doig, who lives in the beautiful countryside south of Perth. From a strong commercial seed raising tattie family, she now has the most modern variety included in the Top 100.

Although Sunrise is rarely seen, it is being trialled in the UK and there is interest from Ireland. It is very early days to even think about winners and losers for this one, but recent shifts in our weather patterns may indeed prove helpful for this variety.

> **Caithness Potatoes** is the marketing company for Jack Dunnett's breeding programme. It is responsible for dozens of introductions including Kestrel, Nadine, Valor and many more. Strong PCN resistance and generally low to medium dry matter largely dominates its offerings. As far as I know it is the only independent British potato breeding company.

SWIFT
Scotland • 1996 • first early

This is a very good silky-white-skinned variety from Jack Dunnett, and throws high yields really early in the season, in a mix of sizes. It is probably one of the fastest varieties to grow, and its low canopy makes it excellent for growing under polythene, fleece or garden cloche, or in containers. Tubers can be less uniform than some other newer types, and the low dry matter should be noted, as the flavour is not as strong as some other earlies. It has good scab resistance, and is resistant to one strain of PCN, although blight can be an issue if left in the ground, which is not advised. It is a variety for those who place earliness as top priority.

Swift is out-performed on yield by Maris Peer, which is basically the reason why it is limited to the garden trade. For me Winston, the other Dunnett early, has more taste, but both are really good varieties.

ULSTER PRINCE
Northern Ireland • 1947 • first early

Ulster Prince gives good yields if high tuber numbers are initiated and developed. The kidney-shaped tubers have a silky smooth texture, but the variety needs to be used as a new potato as the flavour is lost later in the season. It has poor agronomy, but was nevertheless very successful for the breeder, John Clarke. It outsold both Ulster Chieftain and Premiere, holding commercial acreage well into the 1980s, and stocks are still grown today.

ULSTER SCEPTRE

Northern Ireland • 1964 • first early

My favourite variety from the outstanding breeder John Clarke is arguably his most successful introduction and is still readily available today. Ulster Sceptre is a very early variety, fast-growing and fast to put tubers under the plant. The tubers are cream-skinned with a corresponding darker cream flesh, and the eyes are moderately deep on larger tubers. It holds its colour well when cooked, but as a cold potato it may discolour. Ulster Sceptre is a blight-catcher, so think twice before putting it in without an efficient blight protection programme. It is also susceptible to virus and spraing, which can cause internal lines in the tuber flesh.

The foliage is thin, erect and very dark green. Once the yield is under the plant, promptly enjoy the harvest, as it does not stand well in the field. As a fully-grown plant with possibly very large tubers, disease, loss of shape and modest yield outweigh the culinary benefits of a younger potato. As a new potato, Ulster Sceptre has a wonderful taste, being full and earthy. I rate this one right up there with the greats in terms of taste – a proper new potato!

Ulster Sceptre is a cross between Pentland Ace and Clarke's own Ulster Prince. Commercially offered in the 1970s through to the end of the 1990s, sadly this great variety is now hard to find. When visiting a farm in Herefordshire, I enjoyed a very nice lunch with the farmer. He grew 6,000 tonnes plus of Estima, but we had Ulster Sceptre for lunch from his private collection. Need I say more?

> John Clarke (1899-1980) is the potato breeder who put Northern Ireland on the potato breeding map with a deluge of varieties prefixed 'Ulster' – an amazing effort from a private breeder. In total the 'Ulster' series numbers 30 varieties, but many were not taken up commercially.

UP TO DATE

Scotland • 1894 • late maincrop

From Archibald Findlay came this simple but well-named potato. Up To Date went on to be one of the most popular potatoes of all time in the UK and beyond, and has had more than 200 different names (synonyms), causing total confusion and resulting in a nice bit of work for the newly formed National Institute of Agricultural Botany (NIAB) to sort out. Scottish Triumph was the best known of its names, giving rise to suspicions that Findlay had not produced a truly new variety; he was criticised on the grounds that his early varieties were not true new varieties at all, but selections from existing types.

However, the performance and quality reputation of Up To Date was well above this trade fracas. It was a reliable, good-yielding and tasty potato, and the cooked tubers were unusually close-textured and of a creamy complexion. R. N. Salaman, author of *The History and Social Influence of the Potato*, describes Up To Date as 'one of the finest potato varieties that has ever been grown'.

The crops are of good size, but tuber numbers are down compared to most modern types. The tubers are a flat oval with shallow eyes at the point of the rose end. The agronomy is of course well outdated, but comparable to King Edward. The plants are vigorous with large crowded side stems and light-green leaves, and the flower is a stunning purple. A variety called Field Marshall is a russet sport of Up To Date.

Stocks of Up To Date found their way to Cyprus, where it was one of the first varieties to be grown for export back to the UK. It gained huge dominance in far-flung countries such as South Africa and New Zealand, but in the UK was replaced by Majestic. By the close of the 20th century it was still offered in the UK for sale and had more than 200 hectares of seed grown in Scotland in 1987, mostly for export. A humble white-skinned variety, Up to Date can still be found today, well over 100 years after its introduction.

VALOR

Scotland • 1993 • late maincrop

Another very interesting variety from Jack Dunnett, this was bred from a Cara cross, which at the time of its release offered great hope to organic growers. The leaf and tuber blight resistance is very good, and it also has good resistance to potato leaf roll virus, spraing, harvesting damage, bruising, drought and heat stress. It is also resistant/tolerant to both types of PCN.

Valor is a very good choice on early, light soils for organic and garden growing, and if a seed management plan is adopted the harvesting date can be brought forward. Lighter soils may also help raise the dry matter and avoid soapy wet tubers, of which Valor is sometimes accused.

The yield is outstanding, with white-skinned, shallow-eyed, round to oval tubers, which are very large, sometimes too large, so check underneath the plants as maturity is reached. In the kitchen Valor is a great boiler, but for other cooking purposes the dry matter could do with being higher. To a degree this can be managed or varied with the growing season. Give the plant plenty of space to grow.

Valor is proving a very successful variety, being grown in many countries, including South Africa, where it is the No 1 one choice. I would still consider using Valor in commercial organic systems, especially where soils are light or water availability limited.

VANESSA

I do not usually warm to the first early pink-skinned types, but Vanessa (on the left of the painting, with Pink Duke of York – see page 148) is an exception. If harvested early the skins are obviously rough, but when mature the smooth, bright, rich pink skins have a velvet resemblance. The tubers have a distinctively long, slightly flat, bendy shape, and the flesh is cream. There are good yields at early lifts, but tuber numbers may disappoint. It is one of the first coloured potatoes to be ready for lifting and a welcome change from the endless stream of white- and creamed-skin types.

The culinary texture is smooth and waxy with a dark yellow flesh. The taste is earthy and fresh, which it holds well in the ground and when lifted. However, it has poor agronomy for a 1970s variety, so watch out for blight, although there is some drought and common scab resistance. Finally some slug resistance is claimed, but I have seen mixed results. Vanessa is a very nice eating potato and a very good choice for the early show bench dates, while later harvests can throw larger tubers that can be baked. Vanessa was from a Desiree cross parentage, which may explain the positive cooking attributes.

There is no real commercial acreage, as who wants a fluffy pink/red-skinned tuber that looks untidy? For this reason Vanessa did not take off commercially in the UK and remained a garden potato.

VITELOTTE

France • before 1850 • second early

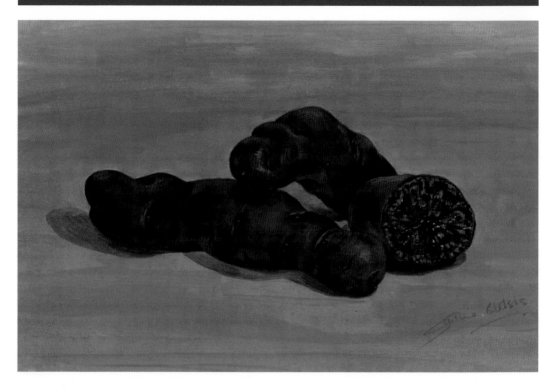

Genetically the same as Congo, a variety that is round in shape, Vitelotte is a long, cylindrical, finger-length, purple-fleshed and purple-skinned potato, with half-sunken eyes that are distributed across the whole tuber surface. It is the only purple-fleshed variety that in my opinion eats well – in fact, it is delicious. The main source is France, where Vitelotte has been kept on sale as a unique premium potato.

Vitelotte has a real smooth potato texture with a pleasing sweet taste, and is highly sought after. You can sometimes buy it in public markets, for example Borough Market in London, but at the time of writing it is only commercially grown in Brittany, home of the seed company that copiously market the progeny in the autumn. In the UK some small stocks are now appearing, and on light land I expect them to eat well.

Vitelotte has many imitators. The great Victorian horticultural author, Vimorin, was quite clear that the yellow-fleshed one, now I think extinct, was called Vitelotte, and the purple-fleshed one, illustrated here, Negresse; yet today the purple-skinned one is sold as Vitelotte or Truffles. I have few details on agronomy, which from my experience is dated. The plants I have grown in large pots seemed robust, but yielded poorly.

VIVALDI

Vivaldi is a white-skinned, round-to-oval-shaped potato. Its key feature is its low dry matter and new potato taste, even when the thin skin is set. So why not buy a new potato? Vivaldi is not suitable for chipping, baking or roasting, being aimed at the punnet and general pre-pack market. Therefore the size of the tubers is medium and they are plentiful. Vivaldi has mediocre blight and blackleg resistance, and is prone to slugs and scab. Its vigorous growth forms very strong stolon attachment, which can make mechanical harvesting difficult. Vivaldi produces high yields of bright potatoes, which look attractive when washed and packed, and its position in the UK market was secured by total support from Sainsbury's.

Vivaldi is a good eating potato, and at the time of its release was thought to be a low in carbohydrate, but as the carbohydrate content of tubers of any variety varies with age and agronomic management this line of thinking raises questions.

WILJA

Holland • 1967 • second early

For many years this was my favourite variety. It is a successful Dutch introduction, which gained massive UK acreage, although it was always second choice to Estima among commercial growers. Wilja will give a large crop of long, oval tubers, with very shallow eyes. The skin can be rough, netted, or appear heavily crazed; this will not affect the eating quality but can affect its washed appearance – Wilja is not a show potato.

The agronomy of Wilja is nothing special. Blight resistance is dated and, of course, it has no PCN resistance. However, it is mostly scab-free and the tubers grow free from hollow heart and cracking. The plants are of medium height and respond well to low nitrogen input systems. Ensure Wilja has plenty of water.

The taste is superb, strong and delicious, just retaining the waxy Mediterranean feel. In an age where breeders seemed to forget taste in the drive for yield, Wilja was a welcome return to taste as a consideration for selection. Of all the varieties bred in Holland, Wilja is up there with Desiree as one of the best. While the acreage is now in sharp decline, Wilja will be one of those varieties grown by gardeners and perhaps small farms for hotels, or those who know their spuds. The dry matter content is reasonable, which means that you can chip, roast, bake or boil it, and it is best used before Christmas. It is prone to bruising in the commercial farming world, and if it had PCN resistance I would probably be growing it today.

WINSTON

Scotland • 1992 • first early

A white-skinned, early-bulking and high-yielding variety, this is an ideal variety for the show bench. The tuber numbers can be low and a bit variable in size, but they come early in the season and can develop quickly. It has fair agronomy, with some blight resistance and resistance to one strain of nematode. It has low dry matter, but with a little less water and fertiliser applied the taste can be quite good. On lighter soils the taste is more developed, and the baked, roasted or mashed tubers are bright and fresh. Winston is an interesting choice for organic growers (facing up to blight issues), and the speed of growth will ensure a good marketable yield early in the season.

WITCHILL

England • 1891 • second early

Now for some confusing text. The variety name, Witchill, was one of many synonyms used for the variety Snowdrop. Under the leadership of R. N. Salaman, the National Institute of Agricultural Botany spent most of its early years sorting out the issue of potato variety names. With reference to Witchill, Salaman had more than a passing interest, so it is better he takes up the story.

'When the variety Snowdrop was first put on the market it was mixed; a dwarf form was selected and became known as Coles Favourite. Messrs Dobbie and Co re-selected from Snowdrop, eliminating a yellow-fleshed form and reissued a white-fleshed one, Resistant Snowdrop. Mr Alex Brown of Witchill House, Fraserburgh, produced a variety said to be a seedling, which was introduced under the name Witchill. This variety proved indistinguishable in all its characters from Resistant Snowdrop. Snowdrop will always be remembered as the first variety, which was definitely observed to be immune to wart disease.'

So I'm glad we cleared that up. Witchill has a creamy-white flesh and white skin, and a high dry matter, so it offers a nice aroma and taste when cooked. Other than wart disease resistance, the agronomy is very poor.

YETHOLM GYPSY

Scotland • 1990s • maincrop

This variety has the same DNA as King Edward and, like Red King Edward and other variations of King Edward, is a familiar friend in different clothes.

The unique feature of Yetholm Gypsy is that it has three skin colorations. The dominant purple is laced with a creamy white, which has red speckles. In all other respects, its behaviour should be the same as King Edward.

Seed is available and I have seen this variety on sale in at least one supermarket under the heritage label.

The stock was grown by the potato enthusiast Anthony Carroll of Carroll's Heritage Seed Potatoes. It is very early days for this variety, but Yetholm Gypsy is a living manifestation of the current interest in potato varieties. Although identical to King Edward, I predict that this funny-looking new invention of itself will have a few more secrets to tell us.

It seems that, under pressure, King Edward does strange things, but the same high quality does win through.

YUKON GOLD

Canada • 1980 • second early

A very good and distinctive eating potato, its attractive tubers are round, smooth, yellow-skinned and with dark-yellow flesh. They have a delicious creamy/buttery texture and a fresh taste. Excellent boiled, they are better baked in the jacket. Unlike Russet Burbank, which will give you bright white chips, Yukon Gold chips will be dark yellow – very nice, but yellow. Poor agronomy makes it essential to get good seed. The yield is on the low side given that it is a relatively modern maincrop, but the few plants I have grown made good-sized tubers.

This variety was the product of the breeding programme of the University of Guelph in Canada. It is a cross between an American variety called Norgleam and a *Solanum phureja* numbered variety. It was the first Canadian-bred potato to be marketed and promoted by name and is now in many countries. Highly recommended.

CHAPTER 7

300 OTHER SELECTED VARIETIES

In this chapter there are more than 300 varieties listed with brief descriptions and histories. It is in alphabetical order and a blend of old, recently introduced and new varieties. I am perhaps cautious with breeders' marketing claims for a new variety, so the commentary against a new variety should be interpreted with care as it is usually derived from the breeder's publicity material. Time will tell the real story of each variety, as I have seen so many come and go – life in the field is very different from life in a test plot. I have tried to include most of the new (last five years) additions, but the recent influx of varieties intended for the processing market has been omitted, unless significant UK plantings have been achieved. The focus is on agronomic and culinary performance. Space dictates that the commentary must be brief: each variety has its country of origin, date of introduction and maturity in the title.

ABUNDANCE   Scotland • 1886 • maincrop

The white-skinned tubers have a hint of a purple blush. Bred by Mr James Clark of Christchurch, it was a good cropper in its day, but like so many others it picked up a poor blight reputation. It was popular with the dominant gardening community, and is a very good eating potato, if you like dry floury types. Many synonyms are associated with this variety, which was marketed by and prefixed as Sutton's Abundance. It had a good commercial run and was grown in the UK until 1960.

ACCORD   Holland • 1996 • first early

This is similar to Accent (see page 41), but has bright white flesh. Although intended as a first early, it can be used as a multi-functional variety later in the season, including chipping. Yields can be high, but variable. Accord has a tendency to produce plants with few tubers, which become very large. Pest and disease resistance is modest, especially foliage blight. This variety is resistant/tolerant to both strains of nematode It lacks the taste of Accent but many disagree – it depends when you harvest it.

ADIRONDACK   USA • 1881 • maincrop

The round tubers have white skin and flesh, and were commercially grown in a small way until the 1930s. They are generally considered to have poor taste.

There is a recently introduced American variety of the same name, which is internally coloured purple.

ADMIRAL   England • 1998 • maincrop

The white-skinned and white-fleshed tubers have a good shape at medium size. The variety has a good pedigree (Sovereign x Estima cross) and good all-round disease resistance that favours drier climates. It is a low-dry-matter variety and produces a high yield of large tubers, but they are prone to cracking and poor shape.

ADORA   Holland • 1989 • first early

An oval variety with white skin and flesh, Adora was aimed at both the early new season market and mid-summer set-skin trade for processing. The tubers gain size quickly and make the required dry matter for chipping; a worthy ambition, but the sheer competition in this area often cancels varieties. Adora is an attractive white variety, with good shape and good yields, but that was not enough to keep it alive and now this one is rarely, if ever, seen. It has poor overall disease resistance but useful PCN resistance to one strain.

AGATA   Holland • 1990 • first early

With their white-skinned, oval to long oval shape, the tubers are smooth-skinned with shallow eyes. Agata

124

has a pleasant taste when young but poor when old. It is currently in worldwide commercial production and is a high-yielding variety with good agronomy and resistance to one strain of PCN.

AGRIA — Germany • 1985 • early maincrop

The high-yielding plants have plenty of large tubers with yellow skin and flesh. A variety for multiple use, but commercially recommended for processing, it can be prone to blackleg in very wet seasons, but has some resistance to one strain of PCN. The seed is mostly grown abroad, but there are some plantings in England and Scotland.

AILSA — Scotland • 1984 • maincrop

A round variety with white skin and cream flesh, Ailsa offers little in the way of distinctiveness and settles for mediocrity in pest and disease resistance. It is yet another 1980s potato bred to suit the growing supermarket perception of quality. Its bold, even-shaped tubers have smooth skins that wash up well for the pre-pack trade. It does have a good dry matter, which makes it useful for processing and general culinary use. It is very pleasant early in the season.

ALCMARIA — Holland • 1969 • first early

A long oval variety with cream to yellow skin and flesh, it appeared commercially in the 1970s and '80s and was trialled by growers due to its high yields of good-sized tubers. It is also resistant to one strain of PCN. However, it was soon outperformed in yield by other modern Dutch types, and was easily surpassed by Accent on flavour.

ALLY — Scotland • 1915 • early maincrop

This variety from the legendary Donald Mackelvie was thought by the breeder to be not good enough for release with the Arran prefix, hence the name Ally. However, this was later revised and introduced separately as Arran Treasure. Whatever the name, the tubers are white, but lightly brown-netted and round in shape. The variety cropped well in its day.

ALMERA — Holland • 2008 • second early

Its high numbers of even-sized white-to-cream-fleshed tubers of medium dry matter bend this one towards the early crisping sector. However, it is also a nice table potato. It has poor blight resistance but is resistant to one strain of PCN.

ALPHA — Holland • 1925 • late maincrop

This was bred by J. C. Dorst, a plant-breeder who at the time was Head of Wageningen Plant Breeding Centre in Holland. Dorst's bold idea was to challenge the dominant Bintje with an easy-to-grow variety. Alpha is a high-yielding variety with uniform tubers. It is a very late-maturing variety and seed should be well chitted. It is good on light and poor soils, and its culinary quality is functional, being suitable for all cooking purposes. Alpha is a very popular variety in Mexico. It has large upright stems and long tubers with smooth white skin and yellow flesh.

AMANDINE — France • 1994 • first early

A potato for the salad trade, it has a low dry matter, a mealy texture and a delicious taste, yet it has patchy disease resistance and its unspectacular yield may not be enough to knock the established salad variety, Charlotte, off its dominating position. Like Charlotte, its flesh is yellow. The Royal Horticultural Society (RHS) loves it, but it does not store well.

AMERICA — USA • 1876 • first early

Popular until the early years of 20th century, America's parentage shows links to Early Rose. A round and all-white potato, with deep eyes and a waxy texture when cooked, it was a heavy cropper in its day but with no special pest or disease resistance.

AMINCA — Holland • 1977 • first early

Yet another Dutch first early, this is a worthy entry from the 1970s. It is very early and offers high yields of evenly shaped, oval tubers, with light yellow to cream flesh. It cooks well and, although it holds its new potato texture in the ground, flavour will be compromised. Aminca has resistance to one strain of PCN, but the downside is its poor foliage and tuber blight susceptibility.

AMORA — Holland • 1999 • second early

An early bulking variety intended for crisping use, it produces high yields of oval tubers with yellow skins and flesh. It has good agronomy, including resistance to one strain of PCN, together with moderate blight resistance.

AMOROSA
Holland • 2005 • first early

This is an early red-skinned type with good agronomic qualities, low dry matter and a close texture. The plant has purple stems with white flowers. It is a multifunctional culinary performer.

AMOUR
Scotland • 1998 • early maincrop

With a faint, part-red-coloured skin and white flesh, this is another low-dry-matter type. It has poor resistance to blight, virus resistance and blackleg, but shows resistance to one strain of nematode. Amour is liked by those keen on showing potatoes.

ANNA
Ireland • 1996 • early maincrop

Anna produces a high yield of bright tubers suitable for pre-packing. It is a low-dry-matter variety, so boils well without disintegration. It throws high-yielding and uniform crops with bright skins, ideal for the modern washed pre-packaged market, and shows very good storage capability. Resistance to common scab is well worth a closer look, and it is also resistant to one strain of PCN. Its parentage is a Cara cross, but it has not picked up the blight resistance of Cara, so its appeal may be limited. Tubers can have a faint pink marking around the eyes.

APACHE
Scotland • 2010 • maincrop

Bred by hobby breeder Mrs J. Doig, the stunning pink tubers with engulfing white skin patches make this one not to miss. Skin colouration is hopefully more consistent in the final harvest than the variety Smile, which it resembles. The tubers have good resistance to bruising and splitting, but there is poor pest and disease resistance for a new variety; however, it will turn heads at the horticultural show or premium market. The taste is interesting, having a wonderful aroma, which is perhaps something to do with having *Solanum phureja* in its parentage.

ARCADE
Holland • 1997 • second early

A high-performing variety, cream-to-yellow-skinned with large oval to long oval tubers, it has a long dormancy and all-round reasonable agronomy. The dry matter is good and therefore the early chipping market may be its best platform. Its overall yield may have limited attraction to commercial growers.

ARGOS
Scotland • 1994 • early maincrop

Bred by Jack Dunnett and marketed by Caithness Potatoes Ltd, this variety has low dry matter but long dormancy, so it avoids sprouting until late spring. Round in shape and with silky white skins reminiscent of Arran Banner, it is well suited to production in hot climates and accommodates the summer drought stress. It gives high yields of long, oval, white tubers. The PCN resistance/tolerance is very good to both strains. A bit of a sleeping giant this one – worth a try, but the low dry matter may limit culinary preference and performance. The plant has purple flowers on close-set dark-green leaves.

ARKULA
Germany • 1975 • first early

Its long, yellow-fleshed tubers with low to medium dry matter helped give Arkula a multifunctional dimension. It is very high yielding but prone to blight and blackleg, and not noted for its taste in its day.

ARRAN BARD
Scotland • 1935 • early maincrop

Its culinary quality is good for the white-skinned and heavily netted tubers, and there is sometimes a purple blush to be found at the rose end. It was never a mainstream variety.

ARRAN CAIRN
Scotland • 1929 • late maincrop

This is a long, oval-shaped variety, with white skin and flesh, and the plants have purple flowers. Probably its best claim to fame is that it was a parent of the great Maris Piper, but was never a mainstream variety

ARRAN CHIEF
Scotland • 1911 • late maincrop

This variety was widely grown in the 1920s and saved the day during the First World War with its consistent yields in poor growing seasons. The white tubers can be rough and misshapen, and tend to be small, sometimes with a purple heel. It is not a great culinary potato, but does have high dry matter, which makes it floury when cooked. This one positive attribute kept Arran Chief in commercial production in Scotland and Ireland for many years, and in England it replaced Up To Date as the most widely grown potato; it was also was widely grown throughout the world despite its susceptibility to blight.

ARRAN COMRADE
Scotland • 1918 • second early

The round, slightly flat, small white-skinned tubers have some faint coloration when the plant has experienced stress conditions. The eyes are wide and shallow. It has good eating quality and is suitable for exhibition, although poor yields and blight susceptibility limited commercial appeal. Arran Comrade was rarely seen within a few years of its introduction.

ARRAN CREST
Scotland • 1928 • first early

This has short, oval tubers, with a white skin and flesh, and very short-growing haulms. It gives moderate yields and has poor disease resistance.

ARRAN LUXURY
Scotland • 1928 • second early

This variety has long, oval-shaped tubers with white skin and flesh. Its cropping was satisfactory for its day, but up against British Queen it had to show some greater quality or yield benefit, which it failed to do. Very low foliage is usually produced.

ARRAN PEAK
Scotland • 1935 • late maincrop

This was a very important variety during the Second World War when stocks were kept back until late in the season. The tubers are oval with thick-netted skins that, upon exposure to light, can become purple around the eyes. Yields are only average but the tubers large. It is a tall, white-flowering, oval-shaped plant with shiny dark foliage. The flesh is white and of medium dry matter content, and it has medium foliage-blight resistance and good tuber-blight resistance. Keeping quality and yield are good, but the culinary quality average. It is a good storing potato and also good for avoiding the slugs.

ARRAN ROSE Scotland • 1918 • first early

The fairly pretty, elongated, red-skinned tubers are small in the run. The crop is early and, like all red-skinned tubers, the visual effect is lost as the skins tear.

The few crops I have grown have been very uneven in size, and the variety is very prone to blight.

ARRAN SCOUT
Scotland • 1931 • first early

Silky skinned, bright white new potatoes are available in June from this old-fashioned first early that did not seem to ever get going, blight susceptibility again being the main reason.

ARRAN SIGNET
Scotland • 1934 • first early

This is very similar in description to Arran Scout, with long, smooth tubers that are almost a true kidney shape. They can be white-skinned, but look out for a purple splash on some in seasons of stress. After a quick commercial flirtation, Arran Signet fell away, growers encountering problems with virus and poor yields. In its day it was recommended for the garden exhibition trade.

ARRAN VIKING
Scotland • 1945 • early maincrop

A white-skinned and white-fleshed variety, this is capable of throwing very large tubers. Unlike its robust name, it never got up to commercial 'ramming speed' and acreage remained low. It was not noted for its taste and also suffered some after-cooking blackening. Arran Viking tubers have long stolons, which did not readily die back at harvest, causing some tuber damage. It was prone to disease, but had very good scab resistance.

ASTERIX Holland • 1990 • maincrop

High-yielding with part-red skins, this long, oval and yellow-fleshed variety has a high dry matter, and is intended for processing. In the field it can be distinguished by its heavily variegated leaves, compact frame and purple stems/flowers.

ATLANTIC USA • 1990 • maincrop

A hugely successful processing variety for crisping, it quickly gained considerable substantial UK acreage. The tubers, with cream to yellow flesh and skin, are high-yielding, can become very large and are prone to hollow heart, so spacing and early water application is critical. Blight susceptibility is a problem. This is a very important variety and second only to Saturna and Lady Rosetta for UK crisp-makers.

AUSONIA   Holland • 1981 • second early

The tubers are oval with a dark yellow, smooth skin, pale-yellow flesh and shallow eyes. A Wilja cross with similar taste and texture, Ausonia became associated with after-cooking discoloration, and a very short dormancy. It has resistance to one strain of PCN and very good common scab resistance. It was moderately popular for a while in the UK and was grown in several countries.

AVALANCHE
Northern Ireland • 1989 • maincrop

This variety has a great name and produces heavy yields of tasty oval tubers with a nice bright white colour and even shape, and shallow eyes. The maturity is more mid-season (July/August), and it produces even-sized tubers that set deep in the soil, which can help minimise greening. It is a very good boiling potato with a close texture that does not disintegrate when boiled or show after-cooking blackening. Resistant to bruising, it stores well and has a long dormancy. It is grown commercially in Europe, South Africa and North America.

AVONDALE   Ireland • 1982 • late maincrop

A white variant of Cara, it is identical in every way except the huge commercial success of Cara. It has good disease resistance, but although the genetics make this description predictable be aware that sports such as Avondale can have characters all of their own, which can show as higher yields or in the tuber numbers – it is thus well worth consideration. Its white skins can, under stress, show some pink coloration.

BAILLIE   Scotland • 1981 • first early

This cream-skinned variety has a sweet taste when harvested as a young potato. It has poor recovery from frost and a poor eating quality as it matures. Its long dormancy period was the only positive agronomic feature.

BALMORAL   Scotland • 1991 • second early

This is a high-yielding variety, holds together when cooked and keeps its bright creamy flesh colour. The lack of resistance to either PCN or late blight hampered its commercial progress, although it has good resistance to common scab. The long oval tubers have some pink coloration around the eyes.

BANBA   Ireland • 2000 • maincrop

A very high-yielding variety, Banba produces a high percentage of large oval tubers, which seem to remain very bright and clean. Its medium to large tubers with consistent dry matter should ensure good chips and processing use, and it is the ideal washed and pre-packed potato. It has a good portfolio of disease resistance, especially to one strain of PCN and foliage blight. It also has good resistance to common scab, drought and mechanical damage, and shows very good storage capability. The seed acreage of Banba is low, which tells me that something is holding this one back; I suspect the number of tubers per plant may be the problem. It also has a tendency to swell large tubers close to the external part of the ridge, raising the greening risk. For washed and pre-packed, it may be too close to Maris Piper.

BARAKA   Holland • 1971 • late maincrop

This is another yellow-fleshed, smooth white-skinned and oval-shaped Dutch entry. Although now dated, Baraka was given serious consideration at the time for suitability as a Mediterranean growing variety for subsequent export mainly to the UK and Europe for chipping. It has very good drought resistance, but its lateness of yield is hard to ignore. It caught my eye for its nice cooking texture, but is best eaten straight from the field, allotment or garden. It is not one for tub or container growing.

BARNA   Ireland • 1996 • late maincrop

A red-skinned and yellow-fleshed variety with good blight resistance, its mealy texture is pleasing to some, but the merits of Barna are somewhat overshadowed by another Irish variety, Rooster (see Chapter 6). With Cara and Desiree in its parentage, it promised much but some 15 years after its introduction is rarely seen. Ideal for French fries, it has very good storage qualities and shows good resistance to viruses and diseases such as foliage and tuber blight, common scab, blackleg and black scurf.

BEAUTY OF BUTE
Scotland • 1890 • second early

Salaman reports this variety to have been bred by James Heron. The tubers are round, very deep-eyed, with dullish-white skin and a faint red colour in the eyes; they are floury textured but with a bland taste. My trial plot had one tuber with a pretty pink splash, while all the others were without colour. The very profuse pink flowers make it pretty to look at. Grown by gardeners in Scotland for many years, it is hardy in both wet and dry conditions, and makes 20 medium-sized tubers per plant.

BEAUTY OF HEBRON
USA • 1878 • second early

The pale-pink-skinned tubers with a flattened oval shape and white flesh have a floury texture and are known for their good culinary quality. This variety has been used in many breeding programmes and is a co-parent of King Edward. It closely resembles Early Rose in shape, but is of a lighter red and higher yielding.

BEN CRUACHAN
Scotland • 1924 • late maincrop

Although the small, smooth-skinned, white tubers have excellent taste, it is a bit of a shy cropper. It was said by Salaman to have a good taste reputation and was marketed by Sutton's during its rather short commercial life.

BEN LOMOND
Scotland • 1923 • second early

This variety was hampered by plenty of small and variable-sized tubers, oval in shape with white skin and flesh. A large acreage was never grown, but some small plots were planted up until the early 1960s. The flowers sit very high above close-set and variegated foliage.

BIMONDA   Holland • 1992 • second early

Used in some organic systems, when blight resistance was rated high, this seems to have fallen away, and it is also one that the slugs like. It is a red-skinned potato with cream flesh. It is prone to misshapen tubers when large, and has a functional cooking performance.

Kondor, Bimonda (centre) and Stemster

BIONICA   Holland • 2007 • second early

Very good blight resistance propels Bionica towards the organic market, and it is suitable for all cooking purposes. A standard white oval-shaped variety, it forms good-sized tubers with acceptable culinary quality. Early indications suggest that this is a variety for strong soils with good water retentiveness.

BISHOP   Scotland • 1912 • late maincrop

This is a pleasant-tasting variety but one that is a shy yielder. It did have a place in the market for a few years after introduction, but then appears to have receded into odd plots. With white, smooth skins and bright white flesh for this inconsistently shaped kidney, it was very highly thought of regarding its mealy taste. It is a purple-flowering type and some resistance to blight was claimed for a few years after its release. It is also known as 'The Bishop'.

BLACK BISHOP
Scotland • 1964 • late maincrop

A white-flowering variety, with round, white-skinned tubers, Black Bishop is a cross between Orion and Kerr's Pink, and not related to the variety called Bishop.

BLUE BELLE   France • 2007 • maincrop

The consistently striking, part-purple tubers are very similar to Kestrel. Culinary quality is good for all purposes, although this variety is susceptible to PCN and blight and that may limit commercial progress. It is very much aimed at the garden show bench market due to its good skin quality. Yields are good and tuber size even.

BLUE CATRIONA
Scotland • 1979 • early maincrop

This all-purple sport from Catriona should be identical in foliage, yield and tuber performance. The few tubers I have grown appear more oval than Catriona, and the skin colour is more purple than blue.

BLUE CONGO
Scotland • unknown • maincrop

This variety has blue flowers and blue tubers, but the flesh is not pigmented like the darker, unrelated Congo. It is a vigorous-growing plant.

BLUE DANUBE
Hungary • 2009 • early maincrop

These are tasty potatoes, blue-skinned tubers with white flesh, but the yield may disappoint. The purple-black stems with shiny, dark foliage are spectacular in the early growing stage. It does not have the super blight resistance of other Sarvari breeder's introductions, but there is good taste from the white-fleshed tubers.

BLUE KESTREL
Scotland • 1998 • early maincrop

The light-purple tubers are almost red in a fusion of dramatic colour. The samples I have grown have been more misshapen than Kestrel and the colour is not stable, so be prepared for some variation. Apart from that, it has all the taste sensations of Kestrel and excellent agronomy.

Blue Kestrel

BONAPARTE
USA • 1996 • maincrop

This is a part-blue-skinned potato aimed at the processing market. It is oval and uniform with yellow flesh, and no particularly strong agronomic traits.

BONNIE
Scotland • 2006 • second early

Bright, King Edward-like, and parti-coloured, this variety has very good culinary performance, but poor blight resistance for a new variety. There is resistance to one strain of PCN and blackleg, and the yields are early but not large in volume or tuber size. Under UK climates and fast-growing regimes Bonnie may show cracking, but could be suitable for warmer climates.

BONNIE DUNDEE
Scotland • 1962 • first early

This almost lost variety never saw much commercial success. However, locally it seems to have a following, and its very flat, round, red tubers with white flesh are said to have a good taste.

BONNOTTE
Germany • before 1920s • second early

This is sometimes listed as La Bonnotte, and is grown on the French island of Noirmoutier. Colourful marketing and mystery of production adds to the legendary status of Bonnotte and helps to make it the world's most expensive potato. The very small, knobbly, yellow-skinned tubers have a delicious taste, but require a lot of hard work to get a decent crop. The very deep eyes make the tubers a challenge for removing all soil.

BOUNTY
England • 2009 • maincrop

This very high-yielding, white-skinned potato is claimed to excel in the early baker content, and is compared to Estima and Saxon by those selling it in the trade. It has Valor in its parentage. Its pest and disease resistance is disappointing for a new variety, but most varieties from Cygnet Potato Breeders Ltd are impressive, so this is one to watch.

BRODICK
Scotland • 1990 • maincrop

This apparently excellent variety is a part-red maincrop It has good blight resistance with high dry matter and good culinary quality, but some tendency to blacken. There is good crisping performance from long-term storage. Under some conditions it is prone to internal rust spot and spraing.

BRODIE
Scotland • 1993 • early maincrop

To all intents and purposes this was another potential

winner for SCRI. It had good all-round disease resistance, but failed to catch on. Its part-red colour was not dominant enough, and it was prone to virus.

BROOKE — USA • 2008 • maincrop

A new variety with no amazing things to observe, it is said to have some resistance to bruising and splitting. It was bred for processing and has perfect dry matter, a white skin, oval shape, and medium size, but poor agronomy for a new introduction.

BUCHAN — Scotland • 1993 • early maincrop

A high-yielder from SCRI, this white-skinned Cara from a Cara/Croft cross is a decent entry, but its low dry matter tended to inhibit culinary flexibility and flavour.

BURREN — Ireland • 1996 • maincrop

The tubers have some resistance to bruising and splitting, low resistance to dry rot and tuber blight, but good resistance to blackleg. The white-skinned oval tubers do not have much beyond a mealy texture, but a substantial seed acreage is now planted each year.

BUTE BLUES — Scotland • 1922 • early maincrop

Apart from its enigmatic island name and rough purple skin, this variety is quite ordinary. Its bright white flesh is striking against the purple skin, and it is noted for its long dormancy, which is interesting.

CABARET — England • 2001 • second early

A modern Maris Piper cross, the bold tubers have bright, white skins and flesh and are an elongated oval with shallow eyes and medium dry matter (20%). The variety has excellent, long-term, stable fry colours, particularly from cold storage, and a good all-round culinary quality, excelling in chips but less stable when boiled. The agronomy is fair with resistance to one strain of PCN. The downside is the mixed sizes and slug susceptibility.

It produces higher yields than Maris Piper, which it is aiming to replace – a tough call! It has a higher percentage of larger tubers, with greater uniformity, and the long dormancy is worth noting. Cabaret currently has 11% of the seed acreage of Maris Piper, but is just in the Top 20 for UK plantings – it almost made my Top 100. Plant in a strong moist soil for best results and to reduce common scab risk.

CAESAR — Holland • 1991 • maincrop

Caesar has good blight resistance and resistance to one strain of PCN. It is a deep-rooting variety with some drought resistance, and is a very good exhibition variety if tuber size can be managed. It makes a lot of top foliage and flowers abundantly. The smooth, bright creamy skinned tubers have shallow eyes and a uniform oval shape. The variety stores well into the season and gives the farmer heavy yields. It boils well, but is not so good for baking or chips, which can be soft. Caesar should be planted on light soils for best results.

CAMELOT — Ireland • 2004 • early maincrop

From the stable that brought us the part-red-eyed Cara comes Camelot, an attractive red-splashed variety with smooth skin and white tuber flesh colour. It is a cross from Malin and Picasso, two very good-performing varieties, is very resistant to common scab, and shows good resistance to drought. Culinary use is suited to boiling and steaming due to its slightly mealy texture. Where does Camelot fit in? There are so many similar varieties that, without any outstanding pest and disease resistance attributes, it is likely to find its market slow to open up. However, there is no reason why this new introduction should not perform well.

CARDINAL — Scotland • 1920 • maincrop

The thin pear-shaped tubers have a smooth, crimson skin, and are pigmented red inside, which is quite striking but not the full red blush of Highland Burgundy Red. It cooks well and in every respect is a tasty potato. There is a red-skinned Dutch variety of the same name, which is completely different and not internally coloured. (See the painting on page 60.)

CARNAVAL — Ireland • 2006 • maincrop

These firm, round, red-skinned potatoes are claimed to have very good storage quality. Carnaval produces tubers with a good appearance and medium dry matter, resistant to one strain of PCN, some drought tolerance and common scab resistance.

CASABLANCA — Scotland • 2009 • first early

This new bright white-skinned variety may prove very popular indeed, and very high early yields of oval to elongated tubers are to be expected. They will go on to make good size and can be fried early in the season, so what you lose in tuber numbers you gain in flexibility. Agronomy may eventually limit potential and blight resistance is low, but the variety is resistant to one strain of PCN.

CELINE   Scotland • 1995 • maincrop

This is an oval to long oval, red-skinned and cream fleshed variety from Jack Dunnett. High-yielding, and earlier than most maincrops, it has good agronomy including scab resistance, resistance to one strain of PCN, and some resistance to G. pallida. Celine has struggled to make commercial headway and has little real taste, but on sandy soils the dry matter can improve the variety's flexibility. Another variety aimed at the dominance of Desiree, it has low foliage production with purple flowers.

CHASKI   Scotland • 2010 • maincrop

This is very much a product of the Scottish Crop Research Institute depth of potato species options. It has Inca Sun in its parentage, and the fused pink and white tubers have an elongated shape. The taste is interesting and a refreshing break from UK tradition. Well done and promising.

CHERIE   France • 1997 • second early

The modern version of Roseval, it gives better yields and has good disease resistance and pest resistance to one strain of PCN, but for me it loses the edge on taste. Like Roseval, it has a red skin and yellow flesh, and the low dry matter makes it a good boiler with a firm eat. Often the samples you see in the supermarket are small in size, but do not be fooled – this variety can become good-sized and even. Some documents suggest that it is a first early.

CHICAGO   Scotland • 2009 • maincrop

This interesting crisping variety is trying to tackle some key industry issues. It has excellent long-term sugar levels, very consistent (high) dry matter levels, and shows good heat and drought tolerance. General agronomy is good including PCN (full resistance to one strain and partial to G. pallida), and also provides a good yield at the right size required. it is very early days, so we shall see what it does in the field. A promising variety and one to watch.

CHINCHA   Scotland • 2009 • maincrop

This is from a Charlotte/Inca Sun cross. The tubers are elongated and the red coloration less striking then Inca Bella; in some cases there is no coloration at all. The plants are tall and very bushy with lovely purple flowers. The marketing information includes good resistance to splitting but poor resistance to bruising. Despite the poor agronomy, this variety has a really nice taste and texture.

CHOPIN   Holland • 2010 • second early

This is a very rich buttery variety with yellow-skinned and yellow-fleshed tubers. If the agronomy had been better I would say it was a higher-yielding and improved Yukon Gold. The taste for me is mixed and I suspect it is soil-type specific. It has good exposure in a leading supermarket so a bright future could yet be composed.

CLARET   Scotland • 1996 • early maincrop

Claret is a high-yielding red-skinned variety, perfect for pre-packing. It has long dormancy, which increases its storage life, and is claimed to be an improved Desiree. It may not have such distinguished vintage and may, like so many others, find success an uphill struggle, especially when being compared to one of the well-established greats.

CLEOPATRA   Holland • 1981 • first early

This is a red-skinned first early. The challenge for any coloured variety grown as a first early is to stop the harvested tubers becoming scuffed and unattractive. Nevertheless, for the gardener it is a nice waxy, light-yellow type that will be as early as any white type. It is prone to blight if left too long in the ground, so harvest as a new or second early potato. It holds its texture well.

CLIMAX   Holland • 1955 • second early

A forerunner of the variety Wilja, it yields good crops of smooth yellow tubers with a nice creamy texture. This one did well in the 1960s in Holland and was exported as seed.

COLLEEN   Ireland • 1993 • first early

An early variety with good overall resistance to disease, Colleen is very suitable for early crisping and organic requirement. Its round shape and white skin/flesh adorn even samples. It is not widely seen, which is a shame, as this is a good entry. Still time?

COLMO
Holland • 1973 • first early

This very good entry from Holland is one of a dozen similar first earlies from the centre of world potato breeding. Yields are good, samples are even and disease resistance is fine. Cornish growers took to this in the 1980s/'90s, but the affair did not endure. It holds well in the ground, retaining a good boiling function, but low dry matter inhibits roasting and chipping. The tubers are oval with white skin and flesh.

CONCORDE
Holland • 1988 • first early

Another first early from Holland, this one is more of an elongated, oval shape with pale yellow flesh and skin. It is a nice eater and has good disease resistance. The name Concorde links speed of growth to harvest as a new potato.

CONCURRENT Holland • 1985 • first early

This variety has oval tubers uniform in shape with white skin, and is a high to very high yielding variety. It also has good agronomy, especially drought resistance. It is a low-dry-matter potato, which is not good for baking, roasting or chipping.

CONFERENCE
Scotland • 1948 • early maincrop

Bred by W. B. Pollock, this elongated oval, white-skinned type made a modest impact in the 1950s. The tubers were consistent in size but total yield only adequate. A wet-textured variety, it is best eaten from the field. Later supplies from stores can show discoloration after cooking.

COSMOS
Holland • 1994 • second early

This was a popular choice a few years ago due to its good blight resistance. It is an oval to long oval white potato, aimed at both the new potato trade and early baker market. The tubers can become very large, even oversized. The variety has good drought tolerance, excellent bright skin and good shape, and also has very good resistance to both common and powdery scab. It is worth considering for organic production on good soil.

COURAGE
Holland • 1998 • second early

Aimed at the processors, Courage produces high-yielding, uniform, red-skinned, round tubers with long dormancy. It is a Lady Rosetta cross but with higher tuber numbers. Its lovely purple flowers are carried on shorter-than-usual plants. It is resistant to one strain of PCN but susceptible to late blight.

CRAIGS ALLIANCE
Scotland • 1948 • first early

The tubers are flat and oval-shaped, with white skin and flesh. It was seen at the time as an improved Arran Pilot, so was marketed at the early-season, new potato trade in Cornwall, Kent and Pembrokeshire. However, it suffered poor drought resistance and the tubers did not come early enough.

CRAIGS BOUNTY
Scotland • 1946 • late maincrop

This is a white-skinned but netted variety, with a long, oval shape almost to a flat kidney. Some good claims were made regarding foliage and tuber blight resistance. It is a good cropper, but after-cooking blackening can be an issue. It is a low-dry-matter variety.

CRAIGS DEFIANCE
Scotland • 1938 • early maincrop

With white skin and flesh, this was a very good yielder. It achieved tremendous post-war acreage, before complaints from the industry regarding its virus issues and poor storage led to the variety being withdrawn from commercial growing in the 1950s. The flat, long oval tubers were of mixed sizes. The plants are an even green colour, with green stems and purple flowers. It is popular overseas with a strong seed export requirement.

CRAIGS SNOW WHITE
Scotland • 1947 • late maincrop

Indented at the heel end, this white-skinned and white-fleshed variety found the going tough once it had been identified as susceptible to virus. It never got much beyond the Scottish borders and was soon withdrawn by the breeders. It has very long stolons, which makes commercial harvesting a challenge.

CROFT
England • 1976 • first early

Aimed at the new potato trade, this English addition failed to turn many heads. Although providing a good yield, it was outperformed by the Dutch introductions. It did not gain sufficient dry matter and therefore its use was restricted to boiling. It was withdrawn by the breeders due to tuber cracking.

CROMWELL
England • 1985 • early maincrop

Bred by the Maris Piper stable at the former Plant Breeding Institute, this variety failed to establish itself due to its adequate but undistinguished agronomy. The white, oval tubers are of very nice shape, and the beautiful arched plant has striking purple flowers above close-set bushy leaves.

DARGIL EARLY
England • 1917 • second early

Smooth, white-skinned and lemon-fleshed, it was noted for a nice soft eating texture and good cropping. Always a minor variety, it battled with Sharpes Express in the early areas, which gives some idea of its harvest/maturity. It is also known as Boston Kidney.

DARK RED NORLAND
USA • 1960 • second early

Aimed at the early crisping market, this is also a nice eater. The tubers have a symmetrical round shape and rough reddish-brown skin with bright white flesh. Yields are good and crops remarkably even.

Dark Red Norland (left) and Redstar

DIAMANT
Holland • 1967 • late maincrop

The large tubers are white-skinned, lemon-fleshed, and oval to round. This very heavy-yielding variety was moderately popular variety in Holland from the 1970s to the mid-1990s. Best results seem to be obtained from the Mediterranean climate. It has excellent virus resistance, which gives the option of saving seed from one year to the next. The bright white tubers, with high dry matter, make excellent crisps and this has been its main function once exported. It is still grown in Egypt today but is now outdated.

DIANA
Holland • 1980 • second early

Diana is a Dutch entry for the early-season, set red-skinned market. It has good yields, but poor agronomy, which in effect means blight and no PCN resistance. Producing good small plants with cream flowers, it has a low dry matter with a close texture and a nice fresh taste. Cautiously taken up commercially in the 1980s, it is now no longer seen, and is very prone to mechanical damage.

DITTA
Austria • 1989 • early maincrop

A worthy Austrian entry, it produces good yields of medium-sized tubers with smooth cream skin and flesh. It is said to have good blight resistance and resistance to one strain of PCN. It has a consistent cooked texture, waxy with a nice flavour, but is outperformed by Charlotte in terms of yield.

DONALD
Holland • 1996 • first early

Does size matter? Well it does if you are a crisp and have to fit into a little bag. Donald does everything right in terms of disease resistance, yields and, of course, fry colour, but the tubers at harvest can be very large. For a new variety the blight resistance is poor.

DOON BOUNTY
Scotland • 1942 • first early

The tubers have a low-quality round shape with shallow eyes and white flesh. The plants have thick, strong foliage and it was said to be a good cropper in its day, but poor cooking quality limited its commercial acreage to the 1940s.

DOON CASTLE Scotland • 1943 • first early

A very early variety, the tubers are part-red and oval in shape with cream flesh. The plant has white flowers on very rough variegated leaves.

DOON EARLY Scotland • 1934 • first early

Very early to crop, this is a blight-catcher, and is like Doon Bounty in many ways. The tubers are very large at maturity, and the foliage is very robust and spreading.

DOON EIRE
Scotland • 1943 • late maincrop

With an interesting, long oval shape but a messy part-red visual appeal, the tubers are very late to mature in poor weather seasons. A poor keeper in its day, it is very prone to virus and never really caught on.

DOON PEARL
Scotland • 1931 • early maincrop

This is a poor-yielding, shallow-eyed, white-skinned and white-fleshed variety, but on my light soil here in Fleet the yields were fine. The tubers are very round with an indented heel that is slightly flushed purple, and their size distribution is even. After cooking blackening is a major quality fault.

DOON STAR
Scotland • 1928 • early maincrop

This was the only one of the prefixed Doon series to gain commercial acreage. The oval-shaped, rather boxy, cream-skinned tubers are bright and clean, and the flesh is cream to white. It is a high-yielding variety (early in the season), giving tubers of good size and numbers. Its culinary quality is good, with tubers showing a degree of earthiness. Yields performed better than the rival variety, Dunbar Rover. Use straight from the field. Dry rot became a controversy in seed stock and by the end of the Second Word War it had become sidelined. However, it was much loved in Scotland, where seed stocks finally ended by the mid-1960s.

DOON WELL
Scotland • 1943 • second early

With its early part-coloured skin (always a high risk), this was the last throw of the Doon series from McGill & Smith and the breeder, John Watson.

DRAGA Holland • 1970 • maincrop

This creamy-fleshed Dutch type is very fast off the blocks for a maincrop variety, achieving quick ground cover with large leaves. Good in dry seasons, the tubers are of decent size, even if final numbers are low by the current maincrop standards. This variety is rarely seen in the UK, but does pop up around the world, being moderately successful in New Zealand. The variety Romano is a Draga/Desiree cross.

DRAYTON England • 1976 • maincrop

A King Edward replacement, this stumbled very early after its release due to poor agronomic benefits. It is not a good one in a drought year due to very heavy scab, while in a wet season late blight is an issue and, to top it all, its yield is not much better than King Edward. However, it has a nice taste and, when cooked, holds together better than King Edward. It was very highly publicised at the time of introduction, with much emphasis based on its Maris Piper x Desiree parentage. The plant leaves are a lighter green and glossier than King Edward, and the habit less bushy and smaller. In marketing terms this was a high-profile flop, and another King Edward challenge receded. (See the painting on page 139.)

DR MCINTOSH
Scotland • 1944 • early maincrop

This annual variety was named after its breeder, Dr T. P. McIntosh, who combined potato-breeding with his full-time job as Director of the Scottish Seed Testing Station for potatoes. Dr McIntosh (the potato) has an elongated shape with cream skin and flesh. It was a reasonable yielder in its day and storage improved the eating quality. The long dormancy is a particular attribute for an early maincrop, driving an impressive 2,000-plus acres of seed in its heyday.

DRUID Ireland • 1996 • late maincrop

This very vigorous, high-yielding, red-skinned variety has good blight and common scab resistance, and is also resistant to one strain of PCN. It has good culinary use but is really good for crisping and French fries. It has very close-set leaves with white flowers and slightly dark foliage. It is one of the latest maincrops I know, so ensure chitting before planting. It is similar to, and in my view better than, the No 1 variety in Ireland, Rooster.

DUNBAR ARCHER
Scotland • 1936 • late maincrop

The short oval, faintly coloured, part-purple tubers have white flesh, and the variety is higher-yielding than Dunbar Standard, with the same parentage. It also has a good culinary quality, but never got started due to its inconsistent yield and susceptibility to virus. It is white-flowering and strong-growing.

DUNBAR CAVALIER
Scotland • 1929 • maincrop

From Charles Spence of Dunbar came this private-breeder selection, and I have to say the five (Archer, Cavalier, Rover, Standard and Yeoman) released by Charles Spence were all worthy of serious attention. Dunbar Cavalier is a purple-flowering type and was the King Edward replacement attempt. Its coloration is fairly rugged, and the part-red-skinned tubers eat well, in fact better than King Edward. The late harvests also hampered the final tuber quality and the storage life is not robust. Its agronomic features are also poor, being very susceptible to viruses. Charles Spence withdrew the variety from the market in 1942. (See the painting on page 61.)

DUNBAR YEOMAN
Scotland • 1932 • first early

This one had little impact. It was very early and of good shape, but appears not to have hit the mark. The Duke of York parentage has not lifted the taste to anything other than just another white-skinned potato.

DUNDROD
Northern Ireland • 1987 • first early

The tubers have good resistance to bruising and splitting, and trials have found good resistance to potato virus Y, but low resistance to late blight on the tubers. It is resistant to one strain of PCN. The original cross was made by John Clarke, who was famous for the Ulster series many years previously.

DUNDRUM
Northern Ireland • 1983 • first early

The tubers become large quite quickly for an early and reasonable eater. Bred by John Clarke, this one bowed out early on with virus issues.

DUNLUCE
Northern Ireland • 1976 • first early

This lovely round potato has good yields and bright skin and flesh. An underrated variety, it is likely to be someone's favourite somewhere, but you do not see it often in the shops.

EARLY MARKET
England • 1884 • second early

Bred by James Clark, Salaman reports two similar varieties on the market. The one held at SASA is oval, with white skin and flesh, and the many small tubers are of a really nice taste in mid-season. The shape today would be considered irregular, but it is nevertheless a nice variety.

EARLY REGENT
England • 1872 • first early

Raised by Robert Fenn of Sulhamstead, the breeder of International Kidney, Early Regent was awarded a 1st Class certificate by the Royal Horticultural Society in 1893. It was a very successful commercial variety and was for many years reckoned to be blight-resistant, but this is not the case today. It produces stems of medium height and very large leaves, the haulms are low-spreading, and the tubers are round to oval, with white skin and flesh. It produces a good crop, but quickly becomes firm and floury when boiled, and does not have much taste.

Early Regent

EARLY ROSE   USA • 1861 • first early

Famous as one of the most common parent potatoes used in post-famine UK potato breeding, it was bred by Albert Bresee of Vermont, USA. Long to oval in shape, with pink skins, the flesh is white, but may have some pigmentation. At the time of its introduction Early Rose was said to have good blight resistance. It is very early-maturing, but larger tubers may be brittle to handle. The cooked texture is wet at early lifts, but rises to form a solid but bland taste. It is a parent of Russet Burbank.

Early Rose

ECLIPSE
Wales • 1897 • first early

This very popular first early was introduced by one of the lesser-known past breeders, J. Harris of Swansea, and was often known in its day as Sir John Llewellyn. Heavily grown in Bedfordshire, Kent and Essex, it was the main first-choice early variety, and held its ground until the 1950s when it was replaced by Arran Pilot. The white, oval, sometimes elongated tubers cropped well compared to other varieties of the time, but had little taste. Not the earliest of earlies!

EIGENHEIMER
Holland • 1893 • second early

This old Dutch variety is noted for taste. It crops modestly, with plenty of medium-sized, cream-skinned and cream-fleshed tubers. The variety has a very high dry matter content.

EIGHTYFOLD
Scotland • 1894 • maincrop

This is one of Archibald Findlay's lesser-known varieties, probably because it has a purple skin coloration in the sprit of Edzell Blue. No outstanding agronomic features are known, and I can find no samples of this variety , so it is presumed lost.

ELDORADO/EVERGOOD
Scotland • 1901 • maincrop

This is the Archibald Findlay introduction caught up in the so-called potato boom of 1902/4, and further authenticity claims. Eldorado was identical to another variety, Evergood, and both showed negligible

resistance to blight. The Potato Year Book of 1907 described Evergood as 'weak and over-propagated and by far the worst of those assessed'. It was a second-choice, white-skinned variety for poor soils, although Eldorado remained in commercial production for at least 20-30 years.

ELECTRA
Ireland • 2008 • maincrop

The very bright, large tubers have an excellent appearance, keeps well in storage and show good disease resistance. They are suitable for dishes where a firm potato is needed. It is early days for this one.

ELISABETH
Holland • 2004 • second early

White-skinned and white-fleshed with very shallow eyes, the long tubers enjoy high yields, excellent resistance to bruising and excellent dormancy. This variety is aimed at the pre-pack salad punnet market, and the marketing information suggests that it is vulnerable to greening if not ridged up well.

ELVIRA
Italy • 1980 • second early

This successful entry from Italy is grown on very sandy, coastal, frost-free soils as a new potato, and is exported to the UK market around Christmas. The dark-yellow flesh is close-textured and the shape is elongated, almost bent to a kidney. As far as I know this variety is not grown in the UK, which is a shame as those I have tasted have been really nice.

EMBLEM
Scotland • 2010 • maincrop

The many very small tubers with high culinary quality are compared by the marketing information to Jersey Royal. They have moderate agronomy in terms of blight, and resistance to one strain of PCN. The breeder is Jack Dunnett.

EMMA
Ireland • 2002 • first early

An excellent-tasting potato, suitable for early baker production, it has oval, white-skinned, white-fleshed tubers with good resistance to the most common potato diseases.

EOS
Holland • 2000 • first early

This white-skinned, early variety has improved culinary qualities, but is otherwise standard fare. Some interesting claims have been made about it requiring less nitrogen than other types.

ERNTESTOLZ

Germany • 1976 • second early

This has high dry matter and a good fry colour, and is thus a processing potato rather than a garden one, but do not write it off for that reason. The tubers are round and can be deep-eyed.

ETOILE DU LEON

France • 1935 • second early

The white-fleshed, oval tubers have a close texture when cooked and a fine taste. The variety has a small cult following abroad, but is rarely seen in the UK.

ETOILE DU NORD

France • 1909 • maincrop

This good-tasting, old French variety was an important variety in France before the Second World War. The tubers have a dark-yellow flesh and a murky pink to red skin. It is on the late side with a close-set habit and dark close-set leaves. Salaman reported a Dutch variety called Red Star as being identical.

EXCALIBUR   England • 2008 • second early

Recently introduced, with very high yields, this is claimed to have shown good resistance to bruising, splitting and late blight on tubers, powdery scab, blackleg and one strain of PCN. A Cygnet Potato Breeders Ltd variety, it has much to prove, but I like the taste, which is not that surprising as Saxon is part of its pedigree.

EXQUISA   Germany • 1997 • second early

A really nice-eating, small-tuber variety, it appeared in a major supermarket a few years ago. The oval to long oval, cream to yellow tubers are small and misshapen at the medium size, and apart from PCN resistance to one strain the agronomy is very mediocre.

FAMBO   Holland • 1986 • maincrop

Fambo produces early yields of medium to bold tubers, but the overall yield is low for a maincrop. The early formation of high dry matter is a key feature, making it suitable for early-season crisp production. The oval to long oval tubers have smooth yellow skin and light-yellow flesh. It holds its texture well, so will perform in the kitchen for all cooking purposes without excelling. It has good overall disease resistance, including one strain of PCN, and useful drought resistance, but is susceptible to blackleg. The plants are of medium height, but the tubers are set high in the ground and seem to green quickly. It is a nice potato variety, but watch the yielding potential.

FIANNA   Holland • 1989 • maincrop

The only potato variety to win the National Institute of Agricultural Botany (NIAB) variety Cup in 1995, it gained rapid acreage in eastern counties as a potential Maris Piper replacement. It has excellent chipping and processing qualities and is very good for all cooking purposes, and I rate it for its flavour. It is a very white-fleshed variety that shows up any kind of after-cooking blackening. The maturity is on the late side of maincrop, the yields are moderate and it has poor agronomy, but is resistant to one strain of PCN. History tells us that pitching up against one of the most famous varieties in the world (Maris Piper) is a tall order, so the odds are that supermarkets and their customers would stick with the real McCoy.

FIFTYFOLD   England • 1882 • maincrop

A lesser-known variety from Robert Fenn, based in Sulhamstead, it has an oval shape with white skin and flesh. The plant habit is close-set with white flowers.

FONTANE   Holland • 2005 • maincrop

This high-yielding variety is intended for the processing market and a challenge to the Maris Piper dominance. The tubers have good resistance to bruising and splitting, a good agronomy and an earlier yield than Maris Piper; the light-green plants have white flowers. A significant amount of this variety is now grown in the eastern counties, and it is resistant to one strain of PCN.

FOXTON   England • 1981 • second early

Around the time of its release, PCN was becoming a big issue for growers, so any new variety had to show some resistance to at least one strain. Foxton did not, but the variety was very good in many ways with a smooth red skin, a good yield and high dry matter. Yet that was not enough. Some stocks of this variety survive, but are scarce as new seed stocks are not being grown. Final yield can be low.

FRANCELINE   France • 1993 • second early

This variety has good culinary quality with strong red skins and yellow flesh. It has a better appearance and matures earlier than Roseval, but is the taste as good? If left to grow the size can be large.

GALACTICA   Ireland • 2004 • maincrop

This high-yielding, early part-red variety has more red than Cara, but less than King Edward. It shows very good foliage and tuber blight resistance, and its early growth helps suppress weeds. it is suitable for organic production, but it is early days for this one.

GARDEN FILLER
Ireland • 1924 • first early

An Irish gardener's variety in all senses, its commercial acreage has been consistently low, but someone must treasure it. The oval to long tubers have a light purple skin, darker at the rose end. The flesh is yellow, floury and tasty. It is also known as Land Leaguer.

GEMSON   Scotland • 2004 • maincrop

Bred by the Scottish Crop Research Institute, it has good resistance to powdery scab, blackleg and potato leaf roll virus, and is claimed to have good blight resistance. The tubers are white-skinned, small and round with a close-texture eating quality.

GIGANTIC   Scotland • 1924 • maincrop

One of Archibald Findlay's last offerings, at the time it was said by Salaman to have resistance to blight. The tubers are white-skinned and oval with clean smooth skins.

GILFORD
Northern Ireland • 1987 • second early

This pleasant, smooth, oval variety was intended for the UK's maincrop market, but never caught on due to its nondescript agronomic qualities and average yield. Yet it has a pleasant taste. Seed is not around, as far as I know, but I suspect a pocket or two remains somewhere.

GLADSTONE
Scotland • 1934 • second early

This dullish part-red variety from McGill & Smith did quite well given the obvious comparison with King Edward. Yet apart from its earliness, wide soil suitability and better yields, it offered the grower few long-term advantages. Its agronomy was poor, the red colour was patchy and the skin had a coarseness that negated the show bench potential. It has a true oval shape with a yellow/cream skin, and although it has a mealy texture it holds together as a boiled potato slightly better than King Edward. However, when cooked it has a tendency to discolour.

By the 1930s the established reputation for quality from the Fenland soils provided enough good King Edwards, while Gladstone, on poorer soils, found it difficult to compete. Originally called Ochiltree when put out in 1932, it was renamed after the farm on which it was raised at Bishopton, Renfrew. Despite gaining two-thirds of the King Edward acreage, it struggled to gain public recognition, probably due to samples being sold as King Edwards. By 1960 it was finished as a commercial variety. Look out for all-red sports that are said to be common in this variety.

Gladstone (right) and Drayton

GOLDEN NUGGET
Scotland • 2010 • maincrop

Very small tubers and a stable texture make this an ideal choice for the modern washed pre-packed miniature market. Good dual PCN resistance/ tolerance is claimed, together with worthy disease resistance. Another from Mrs Doig, it is in my view her strongest offer to date, if you like small tubers.

GRIGOR CUPS
Ireland • c1800 • late maincrop

Grigor Cups (Red Cups, Cups) was a famous round,

deep-eyed, light-pink-skinned variety, being grown in Ireland at the time of the Great Famine. There are several variations on the name, and varying descriptions. Another separate variety named Raeburn's Gregor Cups exists, but this was introduced in 1924.

HABIBI
Ireland • 2006 • late maincrop

This variety has good parentage (Famosa/Red Cara) and attractive red-coloured tubers of true oval shape. It has low dry matter, so chipping and baking may be out. It is very suitable for drought-prone areas, and shows good foliage and resistance to tuber blight one strain of PCN. Habibi produces high yields of medium-sized tubers – one for organic growing?

HARBINGER
England • 1894 • first early

A nice-tasting early, it is suitable for growing under a cold frame as the haulm grows quite short and close. The tubers are creamy white and the yield is modest. Harvest early and compromise yield for flavour.

HARLEQUIN
Scotland • 2004 • second early

Harlequin is a speciality, salad-type variety, a long tapering shape with a red blush on cream skin and flesh. It is a Charlotte/Pink Fir Apple cross, and initial press blurb raved about it, but I am not so sure. It is not a Pink Fir Apple or Anya in taste or texture, although the shape is interesting, and will produce high tuber numbers. It has good overall disease resistance and the plants look handsome, being of even shape with dark green leaves. The taste debate continues.

HERD LADDIE
Scotland • 1908 • maincrop

Purple to black-skinned with internal coloration in the vascular ring, the tubers are very flat and small in the run, although rather nice-tasting and close-textured. The plant is vigorous, tall, open and spreading.

HERMES
Austria • 1994 • maincrop

This has maincrop maturity, high yields, low tuber numbers, long dormancy, and high resistance to powdery scab and spraing, although moderately susceptibility to foliage blight and susceptibility to PCN. It has high dry matter, a good fry colour and is the mainstay of crisp production in the UK.

HORIZON
Scotland • 2001 • maincrop

This could be a big one in all sorts of ways. Its yields are claimed to be massive, outperforming existing ones by a two-figure percentage. It possesses excellent drought tolerance, is highly resistant to blackleg and powdery scab, and has good PCN resistance to one strain. The round tubers are uniform with yellow flesh.

HUNTER
Ireland • 2004 • maincrop

Bred by an independent breeder, Mr Robert Brady from Ballymena, Co Antrim, this pleasant eating variety has a range of agronomic features including dual PCN resistance/tolerance, and blight and drought resistance. It has a nice oval shape, a creamy, slightly russet skin, and cream flesh.

IMMUNE ASHLEAF
Germany • 1891 • early maincrop

Nothing to do with the other Ashleaf varieties, the tubers are oval and stumpy and white skin and red spotting, according to Salaman.

INCA BELLA
Scotland • 2009 • late maincrop

Those prefixed with 'Inca' are the second part of the *Solanum phureja* project from SCRI, fascinating work that has brought a new species of Solanum to the market – well done! This one is oval-shaped, heavily part-red with some internal pigmentation when under stress. All the range have variations on a strong buttery taste and need strong soil and plenty of water for a worthwhile crop.

INCA DAWN
Scotland • 2003 • late maincrop

The main positive delight is the buttery texture, the main drawback the short dormancy of the *phureja* species. The tubers have deep yellow flesh and skin, which is classed as a part-red but is more of an overall blush than splashes. It has a good eating quality and shorter cooking times than usual varieties.

INCA SUN
Scotland • 2001 • late maincrop

A very interesting *Solanum phureja*-based entry, it has very long, parti-coloured red tubers with medium-depth eyes and deep yellow flesh, and once again good eating quality.

ISLE OF JURA England • 2002 • maincrop

Well worth a go as a garden potato, it has nice taste and very good agronomy, including resistance to one strain of PCN. The long shape may not suit some harsh commercial lifting conditions, but it gets my vote as a modern attempt to breed a quality potato first, and yield, while not dismissed, second. It has medium dry matter and boils extremely well.

JAERLA Holland • 1969 • second early

The large tubers are round-oval, with smooth skin, pale yellow flesh and shallow eyes, with very early bulking but low numbers. This one was taken up by the Cyprus Potato Marketing Board to be exported back to the UK, but it could not dislodge Spunta, Nicola and the later introduction, Cara. Despite its low dry matter, if lifted when the tops are green it is a very pleasant potato.

JULIETTE Germany • 1997 • early maincrop

The long, oval, yellow-skinned, yellow-fleshed tubers have a really nice taste – if you like Charlotte, try Juliette. It has quite good agronomy and the tubers form early so you can eat them from the plant or store them.

JUNIOR Holland • 1990 • first early

Although very round and high-yielding, with some commercial acreage, this variety never quite established itself. It shows no outstanding agronomic features, but is resistant to one strain of PCN.

KARLENA Germany • 1989 • first early

This perfectly round variety is suitable for early crisp production, and is also traded as fresh when lifted as an early. It has good agronomy, but seems to be solely dependent on its earliness as a key attribute.

KATIE GLOVER Scotland • 1921 • second early

One of the last from Archibald Findlay, it is waxy when young, then floury if lifted later. The tubers are white with purple around the eyes. The yield is low and the tubers tend to be small. It has short haulms, so is good for cloches and frames.

KENNEBEC USA • 1949 • second early

This key American variety is used for crisp-making in many countries. The dry matter is perfect, being floury and balanced. Agronomy is dated, but there is some blight and drought resistance.

KEPPLESTONE KIDNEY Scotland • 1921 • early maincrop

This minor variety has white flowers with very dark leaves, and dainty pointed tubers with striking purple-red skin, and is noted for its flavour and some local interest.. (See the painting on page 67.)

KIFLI Hungary • 2009 • maincrop

This long, finger-like, white-skinned variety has outstanding flavour when cooked as freshly harvested and early in the season. The flavour is less pronounced after storage. The white-flowering plants are slow starters from long dormancy, but vigorous once established. It is the best-eating of the Sarpo-based introductions and has good blight resistance, and resistance to one strain of PCN and blackleg

KIKKO Ireland • 2004 • late maincrop

Drought resistance is claimed for this Irish variety, and resistance to one strain of PCN. The white-skinned tubers are oval in shape, and there is a very high yield potential.

KING GEORGE V Scotland • 1911 • second early

The tubers are slightly blushed pink, come earlier than King Edward and keep their texture well when cooked. Yields are good. For a few years it gained some commercial acreage, but was outperformed by British Queen. Only light sands bring out the flavour of this one.

KINGSTON England • 1981 • early maincrop

One of the last varieties from the Plant Breeding Institute, now Cygnet Potatoes Ltd, it was one of the first to be aimed directly at the commercial pre-packed trade. It has high-yielding, good-shaped white tubers, with resistance to one strain of PCN.

KONDOR   Holland • 1984 • early maincrop

This very nice Dutch type is consistent in shape and pink in colour. I like it for its taste as a boiled potato, which is very close and waxy. It is a bit more susceptible to blight than other modern varieties, and watch the blackleg. In normal seasons moderate yields of large tubers await. (See the picture on page 129.)

LADY CHRISTL Holland • 1996 • first early

This silky smooth first early has high, very early yields of good mixed-size crops, with good agronomy and resistance to one strain of PCN. Seed acreage of this variety is low and it has not been taken up by the supermarkets, which are dominated by Maris Peer.

LADY JO   Holland • 2000 • second early

This is a yellow-skinned, round crisping variety, with obligatory high resistance to damage and bruising, and resistance to one strain of PCN. Expect high yields.

LADY OLYMPIA
Holland • 1997 • early maincrop

This variety is aimed at the processing industry, offering good fry quality and colour. With light yellow flesh and shallow eyes, it is claimed to be particularly good after long storage.

LADY VALORA
Holland • 2008 • second early

A crisping variety of good pedigree, its white oval to long tubers require less nitrogen to produce a decent yield. The shape may be a bit stretched, but the growth is vigorous.

LANGWORTHY England • 1876 • maincrop

The forerunner of Golden Wonder, bred by James Clark of Christchurch, it differs only in that the skin is white as opposed to russet. It grows, looks and cooks the same as Golden Wonder and, just like that variety, I could not grow large tubers from it.

LINZER DELIKATESS
Austria • 1975 • second early

One of the first modern attempts to breed a new variety for the punnet or salad potato trade, this has low dry matter, a firm but silky smooth texture and white/cream skins.

LISETA   Holland • 1988 • second early

This creamy/white-skinned variety was aimed at Cyprus for potential Nicola replacement. Its rapid and early foliage maturity was the attraction, but greening and misshapen tubers hindered commercial uptake – a shame, as it is a very nice, close-textured variety.

LORD ROSEBERY
Scotland • 1920 • second early

This round, red variety is reputed to have good taste, but those I tasted were very ordinary. It does not seem to have been pushed commercially, being from one of many hobby breeders of the time. It has very thin leaves with purple flowers.

Lord Rosebery

MALIN   Ireland • 2001 • early maincrop

A heavyweight pedigree from Estima and Cara parentage, it is a random-splashed, red variety targeted at the washing and pre-packing sector. It has some blight resistance and good common scab and virus resistance, but overall agronomy is mixed. It is claimed to respond well to irrigation, and has moderately low dry matter, so boiling may be good, chipping and roasting less so.

MARIS ANCHOR
England • 1971 • first early

It has very nice taste and is keen to crop early, but is a blight-catcher and when released was unable to make headway against another introduction from the same source, Maris Bard. It has very light-green foliage, but is bushy and spreading for an early.

MARIS PAGE England • 1966 • first early

The tubers are cream-fleshed and oval with good skins. It is mixed-yielding and completely outclassed by Maris Bard.

MARITEMA Holland • 1991 • second early

This stormed into the market on the back of its good dual PCN resistance. It has smooth yellow skin and flesh, is quite nice-tasting variety and looked set to gain much acreage. However, it bruises easily and commercial growers' enthusiasm waned. It could have been a nice gardener's potato but for the low blight resistance.

MARKIES Holland • 2000 • maincrop

A cross from Fianna and Agrico, this is a utility variety with long dormancy and good storage qualities. The white tubers are large with smooth creamy-yellow skins. It has very good agronomic features, such as resistance to late blight and one strain of PCN; susceptibility to early blight is currently mentioned. It can be grown on a wider range of soil types, and rapidly gained substantial acreage for my traditional comfort; only eight years after introduction it was in the Top 10 of all varieties grown.

MARQUIS OF BUTE
Scotland • 1915 • second early

Bred by Donald Mackelvie of the 'Arran' series, the tubers are round and sharply indented and the skin is white with inconsistent faint red spots around the eyes. It cooks really well, offering a nutty flavour when mature. The plants are very large with white flowers.

MAUVE QUEEN
Scotland • 1915 • early maincrop

The plants are very close, almost dumpy, the tubers are round and usually small with an interesting blue-to-mauve skin colour; the taste has a pleasant nutty feel.

MAXINE Scotland • 1994 • early maincrop

The high-yielding, very useful large, round, red-skinned tubers have bright white flesh and deserve wider acclaim. They have low to medium dry matter and many report that the taste is good. Agronomy is first class with dual PCN resistance/tolerance, and good resistance to scab and drought conditions. It may

not have good blight resistance but it is better than most in this book. It is not widely grown today, but a small steady UK acreage exists, mainly for gardeners. The plant is dark-leaved with purple flowers. Very much worth a try.

MAYAN QUEEN
Scotland • 2008 • second early

A *Solanum phureja*, not *S. tuberosum*, it is thus part of the new innovation in potato breeding. Judge the cooking yourself, but the tubers will break dormancy (sprout) very quickly after harvest. They have a very long shape, with red splashes and yellowy skin. The plants are close-leaved with purple flowers.

MAYAN STAR Scotland • 2008 • maincrop

Also purple-flowering, but not as close-set as Mayan Twilight, the elongated red-skinned tubers have good resistance to splitting and excellent resistance to bruising. The internal white flesh often shows stunning red streaks.

MAYAN TWILIGHT
Scotland • 2008 • maincrop

The absolutely stunning tubers are very long with an almost regal red coloration with white eyedrop-like splashes; there is also a red, centrally placed internal coloration – definitely one for the show bench. The equally stunning purple-flowering plant is so close-leafed as to resemble a fir tree. It is prone to blight on the tubers and susceptible to PCN.

The variety is marketed as a salad potato so expect lots of smaller tubers with a close texture. Use quickly, as this variety has a very short dormancy.

MELODY Holland • 2000 • early maincrop

In every respect this is claimed to be an improved Estima, aimed at the dominant supermarket pre-pack trade. It has a very high marketable yield potential of oval, uniform, attractive tubers with light yellow, bright, smooth skins, good storage quality and functional cooking characteristics. It has a good all-round disease resistance, including resistance to one strain of PCN. Taste comes at the expense of functionality, and time will tell whether it can bear the stress of our climate. It suits a range of soils and, if half as successful as Estima, will be a very big variety indeed – look out for it in supermarkets.

Melody

MERLIN   Scotland • 1997 • early maincrop

A Jack Dunnett variety, it is a Cara cross with a cream skin splashed conservatively with red. It is pleasant to eat with low dry matter, and is functional rather than outstanding in the kitchen. It has long dormancy, shows tolerance, but not resistance, to PCN, and is very good in drought conditions. It gained quick commercial interest when released before being rather suddenly discarded; susceptibility to bruising may have been a contributory factor. Cara probably has the edge in agronomy, yield and even taste, but Merlin gives a much better earlier yield if chitted. Worth another look?

MIDAS   England • 1996 • early maincrop

Intended as a Maris Piper replacement from the old Plant Breeding Institute in Maris Lane (now the site of a very nice Waitrose shop), this variety never got going, but is very nice; if you love the Maris Piper taste and have a scab problem in your garden, this one could help. Midas is oval-shaped with cream skin. It is also resistant to one strain of PCN.

MILVA   Germany • 2000 • second early

This heavy cropper produces large, long oval tubers with yellow flesh, yellow to creamy yellow skins, a good flavour and a waxy texture when cooked, delicious hot or cold. Blight resistance is said to be good, but overall agronomy is ordinary. It is useful for organic growers, and has a very good skin quality for pre-packing.

MIMI   Scotland • 2002 • early maincrop

Bred by Jack Dunnett, the striking red-skinned tubers are numerous and small. It is aimed at the supermarket punnet trade, which, while important, is still a small niche market and customer desire for a small red-skin potato is not proven. It has good eating qualities based on a close texture, and the low plant growth is ideal for pot/bucket growing; high tuber numbers can be expected. It has resistance/tolerance to both strains of PCN.

MINERVA   Holland • 1988 • first early

A very early maturing and pleasing potato, it is high-yielding and oval in shape with a yellow skin. It holds well when mature, but has no outstanding agronomy features and is prone to blight.

MONALISA   Holland • 1983 • second early

Aimed to retain the taste of a new potato well after harvesting, its bright white, low-dry-matter tubers can be harvested any time and still boil really well, thus rendering the new potato market useless. It does have a pleasant taste, but poor agronomy for a modern introduction.

MONDIAL   Holland • 1988 • maincrop

This close-textured standard from Holland has a yellow skin and oval shape. It is a heavy yielder, with up to 20 tubers per plant, but poor blight resistance. It is mostly grown abroad.

MORAG   Scotland • 1985 • maincrop

Another white-skinned, white-fleshed potato, it has poor blight resistance but good resistance to one strain of PCN. It did not chip well and could not find a sustainable commercial interest.

MORENE   Holland • 1983 • second early

This white-skinned elongated potato is aimed at the processing market, where it has found some success. It is strong-growing and high-yielding, with good resistance to common scab and one strain of PCN, and is particularly well suited to 'off the field' production programmes. A significant acreage is grown, but it was never a major player in processing compared to Lady Rosetta, Record or Pentland Dell.

MOULIN ROUGE   Germany • 2004 • second early

This new gourmet salad type has long tubers with red

skins, and retains the excellent taste characteristics of its parents, Pink Fir Apple and Desiree. It produces very high numbers of small tubers with good blemish/disease resistance.

MUSTANG   Austria • 2009 • maincrop

A new and very interesting pink-skinned Desiree look-alike, it has dual PCN resistance/tolerance and good reliable yields with medium to high dry matter, thus aimed at the crisping trade. It has very good storage qualities including internal sugars for late-season processing use. Best performance seen from mild springs?

MYATTS ASHLEAF
England • before 1853 • second early

Many varieties named 'Ashleaf' were around in the 19th century, and the introductory date of the Myatts version is not clear. It has a white skin, quick to discolour, with creamy-yellow flesh, and the texture is close to waxy. It has great yield potential, but is very blight-prone. In its day it was considered to be a great advance and was widely grown. The plant is stunning with vivid blue flowers.

Myatts Ashleaf

NECTAR   Ireland • 2006 • early maincrop

Nectar produces high numbers of creamy, very smooth-skinned, long, oval tubers, and is a hope for the pre-packing market. It has reasonable resistance to tuber blight, gangrene and common scab, but no PCN resistance, which is really essential for new introductions. It has low dry matter and boils well.

NIETA   Northern Ireland • 1986 • first early

The tubers are oval to slightly tapered, with yellow to cream flesh that has a tendency to be a bit crazed when mature, and a firm close texture when cooked. Agronomy is poor.

NINETYFOLD   England • 1896 • maincrop

Another one from breeder James Clark of Christchurch, this first early was commercially popular, being white-skinned with a traditional new potato kidney shape. Crops were mostly for early commercial production and did not have a good reputation for taste. They needed to be moved quickly and gently. Ninetyfold was watery and prone to blight, but was still in commercial production in the 1960s.

NORTHERN STAR
Scotland • 1900 • late maincrop

This round, white-skinned offering from Archibald Findlay was caught up in the potato boom of the turn of the century. It cropped well with small tubers and had some blight resistance in its early days.

OBELIX   Holland • 1988 • early maincrop

The oval to long oval tubers, yellow-fleshed and sometimes a bit pale, are deliciously waxy and easy on the palate, though prone to crazing. Obelix has poor agronomy in terms of blight and PCN resistance.

ORCHESTRA   Holland • 2006 • maincrop

This very high-yielding variety has a white skin and pale yellow flesh, an even, oval shape, but poor blight resistance and partial resistance to nematodes. It needs a strong, well-bodied soil and needs to be well earthed up to prevent greening. It has overall good culinary quality for a low-dry-matter variety, and its future is currently being played out.

ORION   Scotland • 1947 • early maincrop

This was bred by Dr T. P. Mackintosh. It is less famous but did gain commercial acreage and was claimed to have some blight resistance, which was a key attraction. It mashes well, is smooth-textured, and is often used in training crop inspectors due to its distinctive potato flower. Commercial acreage was low-key, ending in 1976.

OSTARA

France • 1962 • first early

This produces moderate to high yields of oval tubers with dull white skins and flesh, which are useful for crisping if there is an early requirement; the skins are rough at mature harvests. This very popular French early has very good early foliage cover, and was exported to the UK in the 1980s. It is prone to tuber blight.

PEACHBLOOM

USA • before 1923 • maincrop

This round, strikingly part-red variety has, as the name suggests, a strong bloom on the small-sized tubers. They are said to eat well, but my experience is that they are nothing special, with poor agronomy. The plants have purple flowers and are quite close set. It probably dates back to the 1870s, when a variety with a similar description called 'Peachblow' was on the market.

Peachbloom

PENTA

Holland • 1983 • second early

A Cara replacement from Holland, the white-skinned tubers have a bit more red around the eyes than Cara, are more oval in shape, and eats well. Its high gross yields and tuber size were undermined by its many defects; its agronomy is poor and it did not perform as commercially expected.

PENTLAND ACE

Scotland • 1955 • second early

This variety, with long to long oval, white-skinned tubers, was prone to blight and was not pursued commercially. The table eating quality was very good, but it was controversially withdrawn by the breeders due to poor blight resistance.

PENTLAND BEAUTY

Scotland • 1955 • first early

An attractive, oval-shaped, part-red tuber, it has a cream skin with cream-coloured flesh, and is said to have excellent table quality and good blight resistance. It is very brittle and not suitable for mechanical harvesting. The parentage includes *Solanum demissium* and *Solanum rybinii*, and has frequent white flowers on dark-green leaves. A useful acreage was gained, but never established; if it had been all-white-skinned, perhaps its inner qualities would have had a fairer examination, rather than constant comparison with King Edward.

The all-red variant was introduced by A. D. C. Main, Windyedge, Perthshire, in 1962. Both are good garden varieties.

Pentland Beauty and Red Pentland Beauty

PENTLAND ENVOY

Scotland • 1962 • first early

The oval to kidney-shaped tubers have bright white flesh, but discolour during cooking and further after, so this is not a classic, and not pleasant to eat. Seed tubers did not store well or react well to damage and cutting, and the usable yield was a little late for an early, so no acreage was established.

PENTLAND FALCON

Scotland • 1964 • early maincrop

With elongated, oval tubers (slightly kidney-shaped), and a bright skin and flesh, this is said to have good culinary performance, but is a very poor storing potato due to gangrene. Although claimed to have some resistance to blight, it never had a commercial life.

PENTLAND GLORY
Scotland • 1963 • first early

The long, oval, white-skinned tubers have light cream-coloured flesh, but poor scab resistance. It never had a commercial life.

PENTLAND HAWK
Scotland • 1966 • early maincrop

With better eating qualities and excellent for storing, single this one out from the Pentland range. It gained considerable commercial acreage during the 1970s, but eventually gave way to Estima. It has a creamy white skin, perhaps rough or crazed in some way, and has not matched either Crown or Squire for yield, during its short life being sandwiched between the two. It is a bit later in maturity than Pentland Ivory.

PENTLAND IVORY
Scotland • 1966 • early maincrop

The yield is very large in both weight and size, the tubers oval-shaped with cream skin and flesh. It has excellent culinary quality from its medium to high dry matter and is resistant to scab, gangrene and dry rot but no PCN resistance and very little in the way of blight. Enjoying a very modest acreage until the mid-1980s, at its launch it was rated very highly by the breeder and expected to be the leading Pentland introduction.

PENTLAND JAVELIN
Scotland • 1968 • first early

Only just within the first early range, it matures well after Maris Bard, Accent or Duke of York, so I make it nearly a second early, which in itself is interesting; a grower can stagger plantings and have Javelin ready for a July harvest of delicious new potatoes with bright white skins (which hold their colour well) and flesh. This very successful variety does need to be eaten as a new potato, as the tubers can become large, which limited the variety commercially, as buyers did not want large new potatoes. It is very popular all round the early growing regions, but especially strong in Kent. It has resistance to one strain of PCN, but watch for tuber and foliage blight if left too long in the soil.

PENTLAND KAPPA
Scotland • 1968 • second early

The long, oval, white-skinned tubers with light cream-coloured flesh have very low dry matter. The variety was later withdrawn due to wart diseases susceptibility.

PENTLAND LUSTRE
Scotland • 1969 • first early

The very true, short, oval tubers have shallow eyes with part-red coloration on a cream skin background. When the skins are set it is a beautiful potato and great for cooking if you like low dry matter and wet texture. The plants are a bit ragged, with dark variegated leaves. It never gained significant commercial acreage and it was all over by 1980.

PENTLAND MARBLE
Scotland • 1970 • first early

This variety produces a high number of small, oval tubers with bright white flesh, which were aimed at the canning market. The plant has purple flowers on light-green leaves and tends to have a low habit. There was some acreage in the mid-1970s, but it did not catch the growers' eye.

PENTLAND RAVEN
Scotland • 1970 • early maincrop

The round-to-oval tubers have rough white skins and bright white flesh. It was aimed at the chip market but failed.

PENTLAND SQUIRE
Scotland • 1970 • early maincrop

The tubers of this Pentland Dell/Crown cross are large, dumpy and white-skinned, can get very large, and are prone to hollow heart. If you try it, keep the spacing tight. The foliage is slow to get going. A very popular potato in the mid-1980s, it was second to Pentland Crown in commercial importance, and benefited from the latter's demise, but was eventually outplayed by Maris Piper and Estima, which were better and earlier respectively.

PICASSO   Holland • 1992 • early maincrop

With striking, creamy white and red-splashed tubers

that turn the head, this Cara replacement has comparable eating qualities and enjoyed commercial success due to its high yields, good agronomy and resistance to one strain of PCN. Samples are not even, tuber size and quality can be mixed, and cooking quality is fair for a low-dry-matter variety. (See the painting on page 96.)

PICCOLO STAR
Holland • 2008 • second early

This very interesting newcomer was intended to provide very small tubers, and lots of them! The tubers, with cream to yellow flesh, are a bit on the late side for a new potato. It has Wilja in its parentage, although you would not think so from the very consistent round shape. It has very low blight resistance, but is resistant to one strain of PCN. This is one to watch if market support from a UK retailer continues.

PINK DUKE OF YORK
Holland • 1956 • first early

A sport from Duke of York, it is 90% faintly pink covered. There is no scientific reason why it should be any different in performance and taste from Duke of York, but many claim it is even better. It is very rarely seen for a variety with such a distinguished pedigree. (See the painting on page 117.)

PINK GYPSY   England • 2009 • maincrop

Another pink-skinned variety, it has large eyedrop-like white patches around the eyes. Very similar to Apache and Smile, the taste is fine with medium to high dry matter. However, it offers some welcome resistance to both strains of PCN, but disease resistance is mediocre.

PIXIE   Scotland • 2005 • second early

This very attractive variety is aimed at the salad potato trade, which tells you that the tuber size is small and the texture close. Bred by Jack Dunnett, it was intended to compete with Charlotte, Maris Peer and Nicola, and I for one am not going to bet against that. The blight resistance is very good, with resistance to one strain of PCN. The cream skinned tubers have a small splash of pink.

PREMIERE   Holland • 1979 • first early

This very useful variety gives options for early new potatoes, set-skin tubers and processing. The tubers are a creamy-yellow colour with matching skin and a true oval shape, and the size is even through the sample. The agronomy is fairly modern with good blight resistance, good handling, and resistance to one strain of PCN. The taste is not for me, however, being a little mealy and bland, which seems to be the price of having a variety like Premiere, which holds its texture well during development and will always retain its shape when cooked. It has made a commercial appearance in Cornwall and, as its strengths outweigh the weaknesses, it continues to have its advocates.

Premiere

PRIMURA   Holland • 1963 • first early

A part-cross with Majestic, the round, white-skinned tubers have low dry matter. It has a few redeeming agronomic features, and is heavily grown in Europe.

PROVENTO   Holland • 1994 • first early

Although classed as an early, it may be later than others. Similar to Sharpes Express in maturity, it is a robust, round and full-bodied potato with some resistance to blight.

PURPLE EYED SEEDLING
Wales • 1990 • maincrop

The plant is open and the leaves a good green colour,

with purple flowers. The tubers are very pretty and elongated, with purple splashes in the eyes. Dr David Shaw, Director of Research with The Sarvari Trust, informed me that it was selected from a bunch of unnamed seedlings supplied to the Department of Agriculture at the University of Wales, Aberystwyth, by SAC and grown in trials in the late 1980s. A local exhibitor, Dai Evans, acquired some seed tubers and it became known as Dai's Purple Eye.

READING RUSSET
England • 1882 • second early

This russet-skinned potato from the breeder of International Kidney, Robert Fenn, has poor agronomy and the brown russet skin and white tuber flesh are not always complete. The plant is large and very thick-stemmed, and the growth vigorous.

RED ASHLEAF England • 1912 • first early

These visually stunning plants have dark stems, close-set dark-green leaves and lots of white flowers. The tubers are long, oval-shaped, red to pink, with bright white flesh.

RED CARA   Ireland • 1976 • late maincrop

This is the same as Cara, but with a 99% red skin with tiny flecks of cream. Some people find that these sports, as they are called, behave a bit differently from the identical parent; they may be more vigorous, or even mature at a different time. Essentially they should be identical; if Cara had been like this, e.g. all red, would it have been more successful, or less? Would it have been a better choice for growers than, say, Romano? Red Cara is still grown today.

RED CRAIGS ROYAL
Scotland • 1957 • second early

Genetically identical to Craigs Royal, the skin is totally pink as opposed to part-pink. It had a very successful short life, replacing its namesake mostly on its excellent culinary reputation. The tubers are elongated, large and prone to splitting, and the skin is an attractive pink with creamy-white flesh. The crop development is rapid and there is a good argument for calling this a first early. A very good multi-purpose variety for gardeners and consumers alike, it is now very rarely seen but is attempting a deserved comeback through specialist seed outlets.

RED PONTIAC USA • 1949 • second early

This round, red-skinned variety from overseas has a fair acreage of seed. Also known as Dakota Chief, it is an early maincrop, and a mutant of the original Pontiac variety. Bred by a J. W. Weston in 1945, it has low dry matter so is not suitable for chipping. The plants are large and spreading with angled stems and large, light-purple flowers. The potatoes are deep-eyed and round with a dark red skin and white waxy flesh.

RED SALAD POTATO
Scotland • 1958 • early maincrop

This internally red-fleshed museum-piece is the same as Highland Burgundy Red. The stunning bit is the internal red flesh, and, unlike many novelties, the crop yield, tuber size and flavour make this a usable potato.

REDSKIN   Scotland • 1934 • maincrop

Bred by W. B. Pollock, Forgandenny, Scotland, the tubers are round with dullish pink, blushed or infused skins, a bit like Kerr's Pink, to which it is often compared. It gave a high yield and stock could be used for direct consumption, or processed for crisps. It was very popular until 1970, when it quickly disappeared, with final seed stocks entered in 1980. In its day, if well grown, it could make a nice show variety.

REMBRANDT   Holland • 2000 • maincrop

Rembrandt produces good yields of bold, oval tubers with creamy yellow skins, shallow eyes and moderate to high dry matter. Aimed at the processing market, it has good all-round disease resistance and long dormancy. It is one of the few varieties showing some resistance to the G. *pallida* strain of PCN.

ROBINTA   Holland • 1991 • maincrop

This rough, tough, round, red-skinned variety has a coarse red skin, and the taste is questionable. It avoids bruising and has decent blight resistance, helped by the openness of the plants. It has good resistance to one strain of PCN, and partial tolerance to G. *pallida*.

ROMEO   Ireland • 2008 • maincrop

This is meant to be a Rooster replacement (it has part-Rooster parentage). It has high (23%) dry matter, good agronomy and yield, but no PCN resistance, which is a shame. The deep red-skinned tubers are smooth and uniformly oval, and show good resistance to foliage blight, black scurf, gangrene and mechanical damage. Romeo is very good for crisping, mashing and roasting.

ROSLIN EBURU
Scotland • 1960 • late maincrop

Varieties prefixed 'Roslin' were named after a village not far from the Pentlandfield breeding station, the whole series being aimed entirely for sub-Saharan Africa production. This one, an oval white with a purple blush, became the mainstay of potato-growing in Kenya, and showed good resistance to blight. Other Roslin varieties were Chania, Elementeita, Mount Kenya, Sasumua (all 1960), Rivera (1961), Castle (1965), and Tsangano and Bvumwe (1969).

RUBESSE
England • 2009 • first early

The marketing company writes, 'Produces high yields of red to round oval tubers, which prove very attractive to consumers both in the UK and overseas.' It has mixed agronomy with resistance to one strain of PCN but poor blight resistance. Maybe its future could be in the production of early, set-skin reds for the processing trade as well as the fresh market.

RUDOLPH
Holland • 2004 • second early

Aimed at the pre-packing market, the tubers are red, round and plentiful with perfect dry matter (around 20%), but it is the yields that catch the eye. Unfortunately there is no notable pest or disease resistance advancement, and the taste is bland. The plant produces an unusually high number of purple flowers.

RYCROFT PURPLE
Scotland • 1920 • late maincrop

This purple-skinned variety has round tubers with a bright white skin. Like so many old varieties it can produce all tops and no tubers, so ease off on the nitrogen and just let it grow in a well-bodied soil. It is floury when cooked.

SALAD BLUE
Scotland • before 1900 • maincrop

This very strong plant produces excellent even-sized

yields of tubers with blue skin and flesh. The taste is poor and the tubers are best used baked or processed.

SAPHIRE
Holland • 2009 • maincrop

Another Dutch white maincrop, this one has a reasonable flavour, close texture and long dormancy, and has part resistance/tolerance to the G. *pallida* strain of PCN. It requires a strong soil and plenty of water and organic matter at the early stages to minimise common scab. Spacing and seed management may also be required for viable baker content. It was quick to appear on one key supermarket's shelves.

SARPO AXONA
Hungary • 2005 • late maincrop

The plant is very bushy, almost straggly. Blight resistance is very good but not quite the excellence of Sarpo Mira. Many think it eats better than Sarpo Mira on taste. The tubers have a kind of pink skin, but the size variation and variable yields limit my enthusiasm.

SARPO GWYN
Hungary • 2010 • maincrop

This has moderate blight resistance, and earlier-forming, smaller, white-skinned tubers with a very nice taste. It has resistance to one strain of PCN.

SARPO SHONA
Hungary • 2009 • maincrop

This blight-resistant variety has very vigorous growth and the late-forming dense foliage is low and weed-smothering. The tubers are short, oval and white-skinned and suitable for all purposes. Tuber development is quicker than most Sarpo introductions.

SARPO UNA
Hungary • 2009 • early maincrop

Very high-yielding, but with only moderate blight resistance, the striking pink-skinned tubers with white flesh are very attractive. I would question the 'early maincrop' rating and treat as a maincrop. Like many other Sarpo varieties it is late to appear through the ground, but does catch up. An even plant, it stands well in high winds with close-set, dark leaves and purple stems. General agronomy is reasonable.

SATURNA — Holland • 1964 • maincrop

Saturna dominates the chip/processing market in Europe, its late maincrop maturity producing low yields of medium-sized white-skinned tubers. It has high resistance to common scab and one strain of PCN, and stores well. Thousands of acres are still being grown.

SAVANNA — Ireland • 2007 • maincrop

This variety presents an excellent appearance, smooth skin and high yields of white-fleshed tubers suitable for washing. It performs very well in warm climates, has low to medium dry matter and performs satisfactorily for all cooking purposes.

SEBASTIAN — Scotland • 2000 • maincrop

This high-yielding, part-red variety has excellent drought resistance, medium to low blight resistance, and resistance to one strain of PCN and blackleg. It may suit drier, warmer climates, perhaps eastern parts of the UK or anywhere that can improve the dry matter levels.

SEFTON WONDER — England • 1925 • early maincrop

This is a round, russeted variant of Great Scot; otherwise the tubers and plant are identical. Very large tubers can be obtained.

SHANNON — Ireland • 1996 • early maincrop

Shannon has high resistance to common scab and good resistance to tuber blight, but not slugs. It produces high early yields of large red-skinned, white-fleshed, good-eating tubers, particularly suitable for baking. A modest acreage is grown, but it is losing out to Rooster.

SHARPES PINK SEEDLING — England • 1891 • early maincrop

Bred by Charles Sharpe of Sleaford, UK, who also bred Sharpes Express and Sharpes Victor, this purple-flowered, round, red-skinned variety did not catch on.

SHARPES VICTOR — England • 1891 • first early

This is another bred by Charles Sharpe, which makes us take an interest. It is very early and has a nice taste, but the low yield may disappoint. The oval to kidney-shaped tubers have cream to yellow flesh, and the plant has very stunning blue flowers; however, the poor agronomy is likely to reduce the final yield in quality and quantity.

Sharpes Victor

SHELAGH — Scotland • 1986 • maincrop

This much-heralded variety from the Scottish Crop Research Institute has faintly part-red tubers with cream skin and white flesh, but failed to make commercial headway.

Shelagh (left) and Shula

SHEPODY
Canada • 1980 • maincrop

A processing variety, it produces high yields of large, white-skinned, dumpy to oval-shaped tubers. It has good resistance to blackleg, common scab, potato leaf roll virus, damage, bruising and spraing, is moderately susceptible to blight, but susceptible to gangrene and PCN. It has medium to high dry matter with good fry colours.

SHERINE
Scotland • 1987 • second early

This rare Jack Dunnett entry is not promoted by the usual marketing company, Caithness Potatoes. The bright white, oval-shaped tubers have low dry matter with little flavour. With good agronomy and PCN resistance to one strain, it is similar to Nadine but has not enjoyed anything like the success.

SHULA
Scotland • 1986 • early maincrop

From the Scottish Crop Research Institute came this part-red type with long oval tubers and a good red blush coloration. It failed to gain much commercial acreage, despite promising marketing and good overall pest and disease attributes.

SIEGLINDE
Austria • 1935 • second early

With an oval regular shape, shallow eyes, yellow skin, and clear yellow flesh, this very good-quality variety is not seen in UK. It has been adopted by Italian producers who export to the rest of Europe including the UK. Look hard and you will find this gem of an eating potato, which is very waxy and worthy of closer inspection.

SIERRA
England • 1991 • early maincrop

This processing variety from Cygnet Potato Breeders (PBI) has short, dumpy white tubers that are partially resistant to the G. *pallida* strain of PCN. It is one of the best varieties for stunning purple flowers.

SLANEY
Ireland • 1996 • late maincrop

This competent, multi-purpose, modern variety from Irish Potato Marketing has white skin and bright white flesh from a vigorous plant giving massive low ground cover. It is resistant to one strain of PCN, and cooking in all categories is good, if not excelling in any one.

SMILE
Scotland • 2006 • maincrop

The naturally contrived appearance of tuber and plant fit its name, and it is the ultimate head-turner for a supermarket washed, pre-packed potato. The largely red coloration is rich and striking, while the cream-coloured 'smiles' are white. Stunning, but not consistent, and multi-functional in the kitchen, the taste is ordinary. A reasonable-sized crop can be expected from the shallow-forming plants, with a distinctive red blush in the central stems of the foliage.

Smile

SOFIA
Holland • 2007 • maincrop

This variety has soft to waxy-textured tubers with creamy white skin and flesh and reasonable disease resistance, and it is backed by a major retailer, so success may be assured. It produces very high yields on good, light but fertile soils, and is resistant to one strain of PCN.

SOVEREIGN
England • 1992 • maincrop

Sovereign has excellent taste, but never really got started commercially, although on its introduction I did rate it highly, and better than its sister variety, Saxon. Its downfall was a low overall yield, partially offset by the large size of the tubers, which are early and good for baking, chipping and general use. The shape can be oval, but is usually a true round, white-skinned with creamy flesh, and reasonable agronomy. A temperamental variety, Sovereign is one you need to know before you grow, and was a little unfortunate to be cast aside so quickly.

Sovereign

SPUNTA
Holland • 1967 • second early

The long, creamy white tubers have a close yellow cooking texture. If you have eaten Spunta, it was probably from Cyprus, where it was the mainstay until more or less replaced by Nicola. By modern standards it is now very dated, but a nice potato to eat if you like that Mediterranean feel. Charlotte is heaps better.

STEMSTER
Scotland • 1986 • early maincrop

One of the first Jack Dunnett varieties from his own breeding programme, this was intended to be a Desiree replacement and gave a good yield of medium to large, smooth, pink-skinned tubers of generally low dry matter, so limited culinary appeal. The good agronomy included very good drought tolerance and good resistance to blight and one strain of PCN. Stemster is a Desiree/Maris Piper cross and an overall efficient variety; mainly used overseas, it also suits gardeners. (See the painting on page 129.)

STORMONT DAWN
Northern Ireland • 1942 • early maincrop

This was a mediocre variety, with white-skinned, short oval tubers, which was offered to the market after the war. Lots of encouraging noises were made and the variety gained some UK acreage, but within ten years of its release the modest popularity contracted.

STORMONT ENTERPRISE
Northern Ireland • 1969 • early maincrop

This very good entry was largely overlooked in its day. White-skinned, short and oval, it has good dry matter and an overall pleasant taste. Producing a reasonable yield, it also offers a degree of blight resistance that is now dated.

STROMA
Scotland • 1989 • second early

Another red-skinned potato from Jack Dunnett with bright yellow flesh, it is best suited to warm climates and gives high yields on well-irrigated land. It holds its shape when boiled due to its low dry matter, and has very good pest and disease performance including resistance to one strain of PCN.

SUNRAY
Northern Ireland • 2009 • early maincrop

This Navan cross is an oblong to short oval, white-skinned potato from an independent breeder. I understand the dry matter is in the middle of the range and the agronomy seems useful if not radical. It is resistant to one strain of PCN.

TABITHA
Scotland • 2009 • maincrop

A Nicola/Inca Sun cross, the tubers are cream with cream flesh and the agronomy appears better than other varieties, with *S. phureja* in the breeding line, but blight resistance is low.

THE ROCKS
Unknown • c1800 • maincrop

This was the main variety on the London markets between 1860 and 1872, after which it was replaced by Victoria. The small, white-skinned tubers have very deep eyes and are very prone to blight. It was grown in Ireland at the time of the Great Famine.

TIFFANY
Scotland • 1998 • late maincrop

A British-bred variety from Jack Dunnett, Tiffany was created from a Sante cross and aimed at the small new potato market. It produces an abundance of small, even-sized tubers with shallow eyes and bright white skin and flesh. The shape is a slightly extended oval, which, compared with Maris Peer and its strong contemporaries, may limit Tiffany's appeal. It has very good culinary quality, but the total yield may disappoint the commercial farmer, and the low dry matter will limit its culinary use when harvested mature.

Tiffany

TINWALD PERFECTION
Scotland • 1914 • early maincrop

Compared in its day to Up To Date for its high-quality, white, oval tubers, it needs a strong soil, so avoid sandy or drought-prone areas. Some small commercial acreage was gained, and it was offered by Sutton's in 1933, by which time it had done all it was going to do.

TRIPLO   Holland • 1999 • second early

With cream to yellow skin and flesh, the oval tubers are very clean and can attain good size early in the season. It is an Agria cross, and it is its blight resistance that is most interesting, together with good all-round agronomy. It cooks well for most purposes, with moderate dry matter, and is aimed at organic growers, where it is succeeding.

ULSTER BEACON
Northern Ireland • 1954 • early maincrop

John Clarke of Northern Ireland bred an amazing amount of high-quality varieties (all prefixed Ulster) but with very minor commercial life. This small-scale variety can be described as having a round to oval/kidney shape, with good foliage blight resistance. A heavy cropper, according to Clarke's personal notes it shows variable eating quality as maturity develops and dry matter rises.

ULSTER BREVET
Northern Ireland • 1972 • early maincrop

The elongated, oval tubers are pretty with generous light-pink splashes, but the variety has very dated pest and disease resistance. A spindly plant with purple flowers, its low dry matter and ordinary taste did not help it gain UK acreage.

ULSTER CHIEFTAIN
Northern Ireland • 1938 • first early

A May Queen/Herald cross, this first early is white-skinned with an oval shape. The early cooking quality is insipid, but more acceptable when early crops bulk. It has short, spreading and rather weak-looking haulms, which make it ideal for cloches and frames, but a challenge to grow commercially. For this reason growers struggled with poor ground cover, which encouraged weeds and greening, and it is prone to foliage blight. The tubers can lose their oval shape if left in the ground to mature. Several thousand acres were grown during the 1940s/50s, but it was outperformed by Arran Pilot, Home Guard and Epicure. Good-quality seed stocks were hard to obtain, and it was all over bar the shouting by 1980.

ULSTER CLASSIC
Northern Ireland • 1967 • second early

Bred by John Clarke, the attractive, part-white oval tubers have some strong red coloration and a good shape, and are worth growing for the eating quality, which is tasty. Never a lead variety, it is claimed to have some blight resistance, especially to tuber blight. After-cooking blackening is a problem on heavier soils.

Ulster Classic (left) and Ulster Brevet

154

ULSTER CONCORD
Northern Ireland • 1968 • maincrop

This purple-flowering variety had strong agronomy for the time, good yields, good blight resistance, and stored well. It had no PCN resistance, of course, but was a worthy attempt. Very little acreage was ever planted.

ULSTER CROMLECH
Northern Ireland • 1945 • early maincrop

The short oval tubers are indented at the heel end, with a white skin often a faint purple colouration. The cooking and keeping quality are good, but blight was its main downfall and the reason for its commercial limitation.

ULSTER DALE
Northern Ireland • 1950 • second early

The tubers are a flat oval with white skin and flesh, but there is some after-cooking blackening. It is a heavy-yielding variety and was modestly commercially grown in the 1950s, but had virtually disappeared by 1960. Its vigour, evenness and early growth lead to good ground cover, but it was always overshadowed by Craigs Royal and Red Craigs Royal.

ULSTER ENSIGN
Northern Ireland • 1946 • first early

Stated to be a kidney shape, those that I had were decidedly elongated and lumpy. It is a white-skinned variety with random large pink splashes or fusions of quite strong red. Poor agronomy was noticed at its introduction, blight being the main setback. Advice

to growers was to lift as early as possible, and it was all but finished commercially by 1960.

ULSTER LANCER
Northern Ireland • 1972 • second early

The tubers are almost hook-shaped with white/cream flesh. The skins have some very localised pink to red colour around the eyes. The initial seed stocks failed to impress and this one never got going.

ULSTER PREMIER
Northern Ireland • 1945 • first early

The tubers are long, oval kidneys with bright white flesh and some pink coloration at the rose end, and a good eating quality. A bit of a blight-catcher, that did not stop this being very successful for a short period in the 1950s.

ULSTER RANGER
Northern Ireland • 1958 • early maincrop

A cross from two of John Clarke's own varieties (Ulster Torch and Ulster Prince), it was not a commercial success. The tubers, with pale cream skin and flesh, cropped well and the dry matter was high, but they held together well when used before Christmas. This was a larger-leafed variety than most of the Ulster series.

ULSTER SOVEREIGN
Northern Ireland • 1963 • second early

Useful in its day, the open plants with dark stems produce tubers that are pink and flat to oval in shape; the pink is not strong within the tuber, sometimes making the sample unattractive. Slugs like them and the floury texture is, for me, bland.

Ulster Lancer (left) and Ulster Ensign

Ulster Sovereign (left) and Ulster Leader

ULSTER SUPREME
Northern Ireland • 1946 • late maincrop

The oval, white-skinned tubers with shallow eyes are highly rated for their culinary qualities. A heavy cropper, it is very slow to grow, and late harvest was an increasing issue during its short commercial life in the 1950s. It was useful for exhibition due to the smoothness of its skin.

ULSTER TORCH
Northern Ireland • 1954 • second early

The tubers are long to long oval, with white skin. A modest acreage was grown through to the early 1960s, and it was highly rated by the breeder, who was particularly keen to get a successful maincrop introduction.

Other varieties bred by John Clarke that were prefixed Ulster were Commerce, Earl, Emblem, Glade, Glen, Gozo, Grove, Knight, Leader, Magnet, Malta, Monarch, Tarn and Viscount.

UPMARKET
Scotland • 2008 • early maincrop

This recent offering from Jack Dunnett went straight to a leading retailer. A white-skinned, part-red variety, it has a nice garden-fresh taste, similar to Kestrel. It has mixed agronomy, with poor tuber blight resistance and partial PCN resistance. Grown on the right soils and with respect, very good yields are possible. The plants are very even in formation, of medium height, with purple flowers on smooth green foliage.

VALES EMERALD
Scotland • 2005 • second early

This is a white-skinned, oval-shaped, early-bulking variety. Aimed at the supermarket punnet trade, the breeders claim 25% higher yields than existing punnet varieties, which must be good. It is also earlier than Maris Peer. It is a Maris Peer/Charlotte cross selected for its high tuber numbers; it has poor agronomy for a new variety, but the samples are tasty.

VALES EVEREST
Scotland • 2005 • maincrop

This variety offers producers very high yields of white-skinned tubers with faint splashed pinking. Its dry matter is suitable for some processing, and it performs exceptionally well in hot climates for crisp production. Of the three 'Vales' varieties, this one interests me the most. It has useful blight resistance, and partial resistance to the G. *pallida* strain of PCN.

VALES SOVEREIGN
Scotland • 2003 • maincrop

A Picasso cross, it produces oval/long oval, red-eyed tubers with cream-coloured flesh. It has resistance to one strain of PCN, combined with a fair level of resistance to late blight in its foliage and tubers, which helps it to be marketed towards organic growers. However, it is an excellent variety and of great interest to gardeners with the show bench in mind. Slugs may be a problem and it is advisable to chit seed for early harvest.

VERITY   Scotland • 1998 • late maincrop

Good for organic growing, this is another offering from Jack Dunnett. It has white tubers with a fleck of pink around the eyes, high resistance to tuber blight and good resistance to foliage blight, powdery scab and blackleg. The high dry matter is a positive bonus, and presents options on the processing front; it also performs well for all cooking purposes. The lack of PCN resistance may prove significant, but the late maturity can be manipulated by advanced chitting and early seed harvesting.

VICTORIA   Holland • 2006 • maincrop

A potato for chipping, and increasingly used in the UK, Victoria has a long dormancy and stable sugars for the purpose it was bred for. It is resistant to one strain of PCN, but blight resistance is modest.

BIBLIOGRAPHY

These are the main references used in the production of this book. While all are important, there are two sources that need a special mention. The work of the National Institute of Agricultural Botany (NIAB) has been the backbone of potato variety information for commercial growers; detail on potato cyst nematode susceptibility in this book is largely taken from its published testing. All other pest, disease and performance comments are more widely drawn.

The scientist and author R. N. Salaman needs a special mention. His work in the first part of the last century was pioneering. Where variety information is solely from his work I have tried to ensure he has been identified in the text.

A great deal of use was made of websites, of which the following were the most significant:

Agrico Potato Breeders http://www.agrico.nl/
Agriculture and Agi Food Canada http://dsp-psd.pwgsc.gc.ca/collection
British Potato Council http://www.potato.org.uk/
Cygnet Potato Breeders http://www.cygnetpb.com/
Cyprus Information http://www.fruchtkommerz.com/hp_eng/produkte2.htm
European Potato Database http://www.europotato.org/menu.php
HZPC Potato Breeders http://www.hzpc.co.uk/news?steID=2&catID=117
Irish Potato Marketing http://www.ipm.ie/
Jersey States http://www.statesassembly.gov.
Meijer Potato Breeders http://www.meijer-potato.com
Netherlands http://www.nivaa.nl/uk
Northern Ireland Government http://www.dardni.gov.uk/index.htm
Science and Advice for Caithness Seed Potatoes http://www.caithnesspotatoes.net/caithness/docs/home.php
Scottish Agriculture http://www.sasa.gov.uk/
USA http://www.dardni.gov.uk/index.htm
Washington State University http://potatoes.wsu.edu/varieties/vars-all.htm

Books and papers

Bartrum, Douglas *The Gourmet's Garden* (Faber & Faber, 1994)
Boff C. *How to Grow and Produce your own Food* (Odhams Press, unknown date)
British Potato Council Seed Variety Handbook(s)
Burr, F. Jnr *The Field and Garden Vegetables of America* (Boston: Crosby Nicholls, 1863)
Burton, W. G. *The Potato* (Chapman & Hall, 1948)
Crombie, B. *Potato Research in Ireland* (Dublin: Oak Park Agricultural Institute, circa 1970)
Cox, A. E. *The Potato* (W. H. Colleridge, 1967)
Daly, M. E. *The Famine in Ireland* (Dublin Historical Association, 1967)
Davidson, W. D. *The History of Potato Varieties* (Journal of the Department of Agriculture, Eire, 1933)
    The Rejuvenation of Champion (ibid, 1928)
    Potato Growing for Seed Purposes (ibid, 1936)
Dean, A. *Vegetable Culture* (Macmillan & Co, 1917)
Dunnett, J. A. *Scottish Potato Breeders Harvest* (Dunnett, 2000)
    Scottish Potato Breeders Harvest Part Two (Dunnett, 2009)
Farmers Weekly, article 'Five New Potatoes' (1942)
Fuller, J. *The Potato Caterer's Manual* (Pitmans & Son, 1963)
Gallie, R. J. L. *The Scottish Plant Breeding Station: A Historical Review* (1954)
Gardeners, The (magazine, volumes 1875, 1876, 1877)
Gault, S. M. *Vegetables for the Garden and Exhibition* (W. H. & L. Colleridge, 1956)

Good, W. G. *Allotment Gardening* (The Gresham Publishing Company, 1922)

Grubb, E. H. & Guilford, W. S. *The Potato* (USA: Doubleday, Page & Co, 1912)

Gussen, G. *The Production and Utilisation of Potatoes in Ireland* (Dublin: Department of Agriculture & Fisheries, date unknown)

Harris, P. M. *The Potato Crop* (Chapman & Hall, 1978)

Hellyer, A. G. *The Amateur Gardener* (W. H. & L. Colleridge, 1948)

Kehoe, H. W. and Dowley, L. J. *Description of New Potato Varieties* (Dublin: Oak Park Research Centre, unpublished)

Lawson, P. *The Agriculturist's Manual* (Blackwood & Sons, 1836)

Macarthur, A. W. *Fifty Years of Potato Breeding at the Scottish Plant Breeding Station* (Journal of the National Association of Seed Potato Merchants, 1970)

Macdonald, D. M. *A Classification of Potato Varieties in the Reference Collection at East Craigs, Edinburgh* (1991)

McIntosh, T. P. *The Potato: Its History, Varieties, Culture and Diseases* (Oliver & Boyd, 1927)

McKay, R. *Potato Diseases* (Irish Potato Marketing, 1955)

Macself, A. J. *The Vegetable Grower's Treasury* (W. H. & L Colleridge, 1930)

Middleton, C. H. *Mr Middleton's Gardening Book* (Daily Express, 1941)

Ministry of Agriculture, UK Bulletin 94 Potatoes 1938, 1957, 1961, 1965, 1972

Ministry of Agriculture & Fisheries, UK Collected Leaflets on Cultivation and Diseases of Potatoes 1921

NIAB Potato Variety Publications, 1924 to 2011

NIVAA Netherlands Catalogue of Potato Varieties, 1980 to 1997

O'Grada, C. *Ireland Before and After Famine* (Manchester University Press, 1988)

O'Neill, T. P. *The Scientific Investigation of Failure of the Potato Crop In Ireland 1845/46* (Irish Historical Studies, 1946)

O'Rourke, Can J. O. *The Great Irish Potato Famine* (Veritas Press, 1874; reprinted 1989)

Poirteir, C. *The Great Irish Famine* (RTE, Mercier Press, 1995)

Potato Marketing Board UK (aka British Potato Council), *Historical Notes on Potato Culture and Marketing* (PMB, 1968)

   British Atlas of Potato Varieties (1968)

   Crop Statistics (yearly reports, 1950 to date)

   Potato Diseases (1993)

Potato Yearbook, The 1996 onwards (ACT Publishing)

Romans, A. *The Potato Book* (Frances Lincoln, 2005)

Royal Horticultural Society *The Garden* (1875, 1876)

Salaman, R. N. *Potato Varieties* (Cambridge University Press, 1926)

   Potatoes: A Retrospective 1918-1939 (10th Findlay Memorial Lecture)

Salaman, R. N., revised and edited by Hughes, J. C. *The History and Social Influence of the Potato* (1985)

Scotland Seed Potato Development Council, *The Natural Home for Seed Potatoes* (1995)

Shewell-Cooper, W. E. *The ABD of Vegetable Gardening* (English University Press, 1941)

Simons, J. *The Vegetable Grower's Handbook Volume 1* (Penguin, 1945)

Sparks, G. A. *Identification of New Zealand Potato Cultivars* (MAF NZ, 1990)

Sutton's Seeds catalogues, 1877-1933

Van Der Zaag, D. E. *Potatoes and their Cultivation in the Netherlands* (Ministry of Agriculture, 1980)

Vimorin and Andreaux *The Vegetable Garden* (1905)

Whitbred, McIntosh and Findlay *The Potato in Health and Disease* (Oliver & Boyd, 1953)

Wilde, W. R. *An Introduction and Time of General Use of the Potato in Ireland* (Proceedings of the Royal Irish Academy, Vol XI)

Wilson, A. M. *The Story of The Potato Through Illustrated Varieties* (Alan Wilson, 1993)

Woodham Smith, C. *The Great Hunger Ireland 1845-50* (Hamish Hamilton, 1962)

Wright, H. J. and Adsett, W. H. *The Potato Year Book* (National Potato Society, 1907)

INDEX